1929   1953

Hoover, Roosevelt & Truman

ROURKE'S COMPLETE HISTORY OF OUR PRESIDENTS ENCYCLOPEDIA

Volume 9

Kelli L. Hicks, Editor

Ypsilanti District Library
5577 Whittaker Road
Ypsilanti, MI 48197

Rourke Publishing

Vero Beach, Florida 32964 | www.rourkepublishing.com

© 2009 Rourke Publishing LLC

All rights reserved. No part of this book may be reproduced or utilized in any form or by any means, electronic or mechanical including photocopying, recording, or by any information storage and retrieval system without permission in writing from the publisher.

www.rourkepublishing.com

PHOTO CREDITS: Pages 4, 6, 8, 9, 10, 11, 12, 13, 14, 15, 16, 17, 18, 20, 21, 22, 23, 28, 32, 34, 35, 38, 39, 44, 48, 52 © Library of Congress; Pages 5, 24, 25, 27, 31, 37 © Franklin D. Roosevelt Library; Pages 7, 19, 50 © Herbert Hoover Library; Pages 40, 41, 42, 43, 45, 46, 49, 53 © Harry S. Truman Library; Page 51 © National Nuclear Security Administration/Nevada Site Office

Editor: Kelli L. Hicks

Cover and interior design by Nicola Stratford, bdpublishing.com

Library of Congress Cataloging-in-Publication Data

Rourke's Complete History of Our Presidents Encyclopedia / Kelli L. Hicks
    p. cm.
Includes bibliographical references and index.
Summary: Discusses the political lives and times of the men who served as United States presidents, their administrations, and the events which occurred during their tenures.
  Set ISBN 978-1-60694-293-2
  Title ISBN 978-1-60694-302-1
1. Presidents—United States—Juvenile literature.

Printed in the USA
CG/CG

www.rourkepublishing.com – rourke@rourkepublishing.com
Post Office Box 3328, Vero Beach, FL 32964

From Prosperity to War 4

Herbert Hoover (1929–1933) 10

Franklin D. Roosevelt (1933–1945) 20

Harry S. Truman (1945–1953) 38

The Presidency at the Dawn of the Atomic Age 50

Cabinet Members 54

Timeline 56

Presidents of the United States 60

Index 62

Further Reading 64

From Prosperity to War

During the 1928 presidential campaign, the nominee for the Republican Party, Herbert Hoover, promised Americans that there would be a "chicken in every pot, and a car in every garage." It was a way of saying that the prosperity of the 1920s could be guaranteed by electing another Republican president. The American voters agreed and elected Hoover, giving him a landslide victory.

People closely identified the Republican presidents of the 1920s with the nation's good economic times. Both Presidents Warren Harding who served from 1921 to 1923, and Calvin Coolidge, who served from 1923 to 1929, believed that the American economy was best if left alone, without any interference from the government in Washington, D.C. They did as little concerning this issue as possible during their presidencies believing that private industry would guide the nation to prosperity on its own.

Herbert Hoover campaigned with great success, winning the presidency with 58 percent of the vote.

Hungry New Yorkers wait in breadlines during the Great Depression.

LINE FOR
1¢ RESTAURANT
20 MEALS FOR $1
DONATIONS INVITED
HELP FEED THE HUNGRY
$1 WILL FEED 20
1¢ RESTAURANT
107 W. 43rd ST.
D.S.

From Prosperity to War

President Herbert Hoover was not as "do-nothing" as his two predecessors. He believed that government should serve as a kind of referee between industries and as a promoter of economic cooperation. He did not believe, however, that government had a more active role to play than that. He thought that, in the end, business should manage its own affairs.

Crash!

In October 1929, the Hoover Republican philosophy was put to the test. The U.S. stock market crashed, and in the wake of this event, the American, and consequently the world economy, went into a tailspin. Within three years, unemployment affected nearly 13 million Americans, 10 percent of the population, and the economy seemed on the brink of collapse.

At first, President Hoover predicted that the economy would correct itself and get back to normal. When it failed to do so, he reluctantly agreed that the federal government would need to get involved to make recovery happen. Hoover, however, did not have the chance to test his new approach. The voters turned him out of office in 1932 and elected a Democratic president.

Franklin D. Roosevelt, unlike Hoover, was willing to try anything to fix the economy. If one approach did not work, he tried another. While Hoover had worried about what to do, Roosevelt proved to be an activist president, ready to use the power of his office and the federal government to help the nation.

The Activist Presidency

Roosevelt changed the presidency forever. He expanded and strengthened the presidential office during the Great Depression of the 1930s and again in the difficult years of America's involvement in World War II (1941–1945).

Franklin Delano Roosevelt delivers his inaugural address from the south portico of the White House.

Words to Know

Great Depression (GRAYT di-PRESH-uhn): The economic collapse that eventually affected the entire world, starting in 1929 and lasting through the 1930s.

World War II (WURLD WOR TOO): The worldwide conflict fought between 1939 and 1945. The United States became involved against Japan, Italy, and Germany in 1941.

Black Tuesday

During the 1920s, the stock market became the symbol of American prosperity. About 10 percent of the nation's households, which equated to some 4 million Americans, owned stock in 1929. They believed what the financier John J. Raskob had written in an article in the Ladies' Home Journal: "Everyone Ought to Be Rich."

Many people, however, were buying stock on margin. That is, stockbrokers were allowing them to borrow money to pay up to 75 percent of the purchase price of stock. If prices dropped, many investors would not be able to pay their debts. But few people seriously considered that possibility. As long as the prices kept rising, as they did throughout 1928 and 1929, everyone would be a winner.

Then came Black Tuesday: October 29, 1929. The stock process had been sliding since early September. But on October 29, the bubble burst. Investors began to sell their stocks to pay off debts, and panic set in. Overnight, millions of shares were sold, and the value of stocks dropped by about 40 percent. Many people were wiped out. A few even committed suicide.

The prosperity of the 1920s, at least in the stock market, had ended. Ahead lay the Great Depression, a huge economic downturn that would leave millions unemployed and shake the foundations of democratic society.

Gloom sets in on the trading floor of the New York Stock Exchange just after the crash of 1929.

8 From Prosperity to War

Roosevelt wanted the government to get involved in the affairs of business and labor. Unlike the Republicans, he was suspicious of business. He believed in the American economic system, but he also thought that business was out for its own good and that the government should be the watchdog that looked out for ordinary people.

The War Presidency

The vast number of government programs created during Roosevelt's first two terms as president, in the 1930s, increased the size and power of government. But the biggest increase in presidential power came as a result of America's role in World War II.

World War II posters such as this one by artist Henry Koerner promoted strength in the unity of the allied countries.

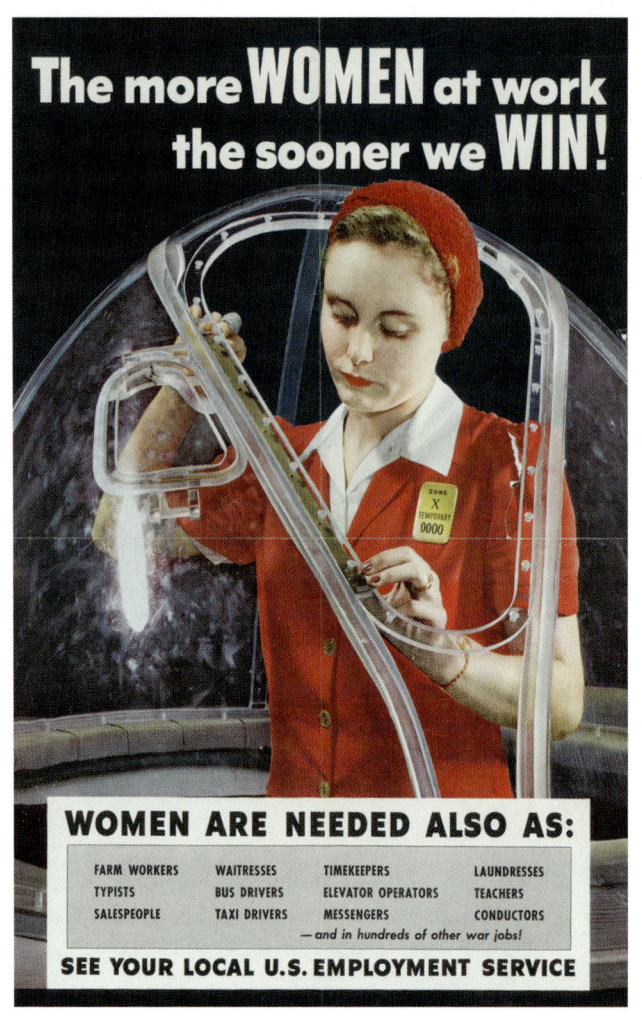

A war poster depicts a woman working in an airplane factory.

During the war, the president became the commander of a vast military machine of 16 million men and women. A gigantic bureaucracy, in both the military and the civilian parts of the government, was needed to run this machine. By the time the war ended in 1945, a big military had become a permanent part of the structure of U.S. government. As a result of the war, the United States was now a major world power, with global responsibilities. And the American president was now one of the most powerful leaders on Earth.

The Atomic Age

A world-shaking development enhanced the power of the presidency in the early 1940s: the invention of nuclear power. President Roosevelt had authorized scientists to develop a nuclear bomb as part of America's defenses during the war. In 1945, his successor, President Harry Truman, decided to use the new discovery against the Japanese to force them to surrender.

Now, the American president had the most powerful weapon in the world at his disposal. Presidential power had reached unheard of heights.

Truman was the first, and so far only, American president to use nuclear weapons. Each president since Truman has had a vast arsenal of nuclear weapons available. But since 1945, American presidents have not used their nuclear weapons. Potential enemies, however, remain aware that they exist.

The Great Depression and war converted the presidency from the office that it was in the 1920s, when Calvin Coolidge worked only four hours a day and had time to take naps, to what it is today: a vast, modern institution that presides over the American government and controls the most destructive groups of weapons known in human history.

Atomic bombs sent huge clouds into the sky, as seen in the aerial photograph of this test explosion.

Herbert Hoover

Herbert Hoover was one of the hardest working presidents the United States ever had. His inauguration, on March 4, 1929, greeted him with joyous celebration by a nation at peace and at the height of prosperity.

Four years later, Herbert Hoover left Washington, D.C., a broken and bitter man, defeated overwhelmingly for reelection and widely blamed for the events that had plunged the nation into a disastrous depression. Millions of Americans were out of work, and homeless, hungry people roamed the country looking for jobs. Hoover, a man who had enjoyed nothing but success in everything that he had attempted previously, presided over one of the unhappiest presidencies in American History.

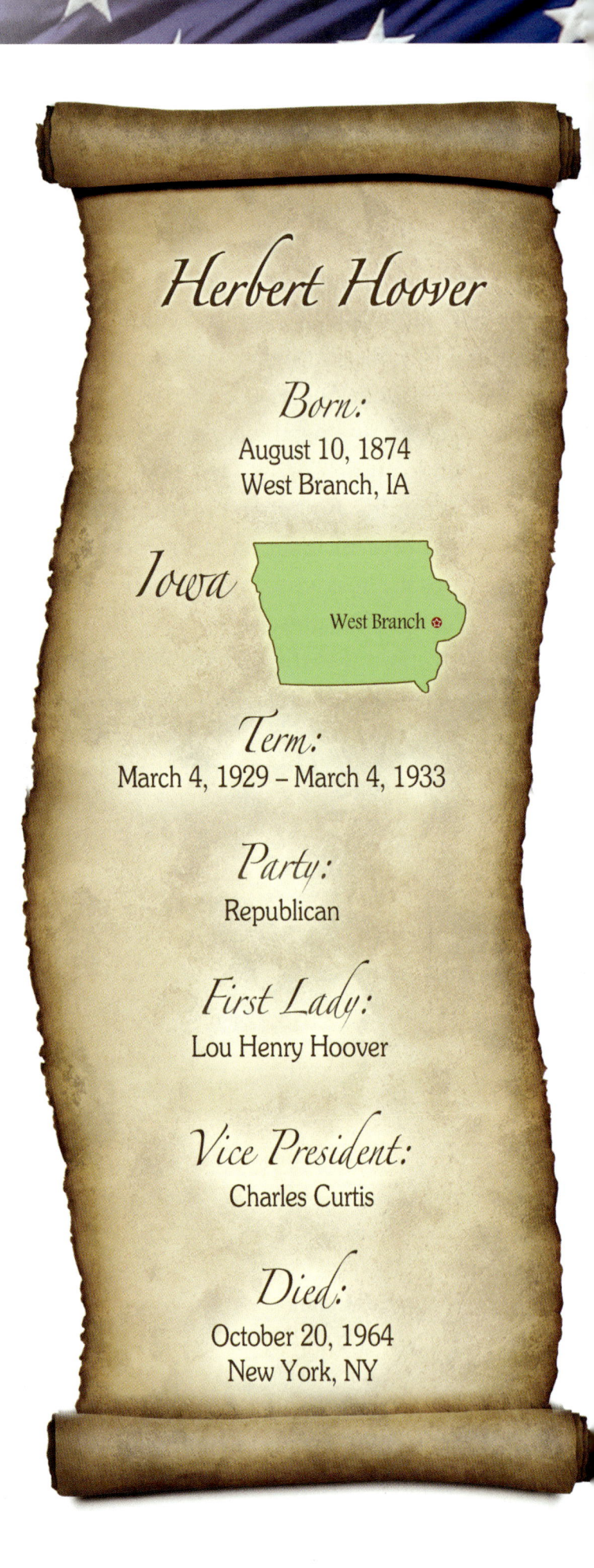

Vice President Charles Curtis

Herbert Hoover

Born:
August 10, 1874
West Branch, IA

Iowa — West Branch

Term:
March 4, 1929 – March 4, 1933

Party:
Republican

First Lady:
Lou Henry Hoover

Vice President:
Charles Curtis

Died:
October 20, 1964
New York, NY

Herbert Hoover

31st President of the United States

Herbert Hoover

Early Life

Herbert Clark Hoover was born in West Branch, Iowa, on August 10, 1874, the second of three children of Jesse and Huldah Minthorn Hoover. The Hoovers were Quakers whose ancestors had migrated to America from Switzerland in the 1730s and 1740s.

By the time Herbert was nine years old, both his parents had died. In 1884, he and his brother and sister went to live with relatives in Oregon. In his memoirs, Hoover would recall a happy life with his Uncle John Minthorn and his Aunt Millie. It was a time filled with laughter and play and many outdoor activities.

While working as a teenager in his uncle's land-settlement business, Herbert became interested in mining as a profession. In 1891, determined to study mining engineering, he was one of the first students to enroll at the new Leland Stanford Jr. University (now Stanford University), in Palo Alto, California.

When Hoover graduated from college in 1895, mining engineering jobs were scarce, so the young man accepted a position pushing a cart in a gold mine, where he worked for $2 an hour, seven days a week. Hoover eventually got a better job in an engineering company. Early in 1896, his boss recommended him to work on a mining project in Australia. The young engineer sailed overseas in search of adventure and success.

International Travel and Work

Hoover's engineering work at the gold mine in Australia was so successful that he soon received an offer for a job in China. Before leaving for China, however, he wired a proposal of marriage to Lou Henry, his sweetheart from his Stanford days. She accepted by cable. They were married on February 10, 1899, and sailed for China the same day.

In China, Hoover organized the government's mining department and helped the Chinese discover valuable coal fields and industrial minerals. By 1908, Hoover had enough experience to open his own mining firm, with offices in the United States, England, and Russia. The firm provided consulting services to mining companies on technical and organizational questions. By the time he was 40, Hoover was a rich man who was highly respected as an engineer and an organizational genius.

Herbert Hoover was well traveled as a young man.

Herbert Hoover

Humanitarian Work

When World War I broke out in Europe in 1914, Herbert Hoover was at work in his office in London, England. Because of his organizational skills and reputation for efficiency, the American ambassador approached Hoover and asked him to help organize a relief effort for the Belgian people. The German army had invaded Belgium in 1914 as it marched toward France. The British had blocked the coast of Belgium to try to stop the Germans, and as a result, food supplies could not get through to the Belgium people, who now faced starvation.

Hoover organized the Committee for the Relief of Belgium. Because the United States was not yet involved in the war, Hoover was a neutral representative. He was able to convince both the British and the Germans to allow food supplies through the blockade. By the end of the war, more than 5 million tons of food had been delivered to war torn areas of Belgium and northern France.

The United States Food Administration urged merchants to display signs such as this one encouraging Americans to conserve food.

Hoover took no salary for his relief work. When the United States entered World War I in 1917, he returned to America and accepted the position of food administrator for the United States. He was responsible for creating programs to increase food production and to ration, or divide, the available food during the course of the War.

When World War I ended, in 1918, Hoover was put in charge of providing food relief for all of Europe. He received credit for saving millions of lives because of his tireless efforts on behalf of starving people. To the people of Europe, Herbert Hoover was a hero.

Secretary of Commerce

The brilliant organizer of food relief was clearly someone whose skills had to be used in higher positions. In 1921, the new Republican president, Warren G. Harding, appointed Hoover to the cabinet position of secretary of commerce.

Herbert Hoover quickly applied his many talents to his new position. Amazed officials in the government began to call him "secretary of everything." As secretary of commerce, one of his major objectives was to improve relations between government and business, and among businesses themselves. Hoover encouraged businesses to establish cooperative organization through which they could share information and reduce the negative effects of excessive competition.

Herbert Hoover

Herbert Hoover's radio conferences played a major role in the early development of broadcasting.

He also pushed for the adoption of standards and sizes for hundreds of products, thus improving efficiency and lowering cost. Hoover was concerned about the nation's water resources and helped lay the groundwork for irrigation and power projects that were later built in Colorado, California, and the Pacific Northwest. Hoover was also eager to set up the rules and procedures for public ownership of radio broadcasting channels, and he established regulatory laws concerning American civil aviation.

Hoover remained as secretary of commerce after the death of President Harding in 1923. Calvin Coolidge, who succeeded Harding after he died, won the presidential election in his own right in 1924. In 1927, however, Coolidge announced that he would not run for another term in office. Thus, early in 1928, Hoover quit the cabinet in order to pursue the Republican nomination for president.

The 1928 Election

Herbert Hoover was so dominating a figure that no serious challenge to his candidacy emerged. He received the nomination by the Republican Convention in June of 1928. The convention selected Senator Charles Curtis of Kansas as the Republican vice-presidential candidate.

Hoover's platform, the promises and plans that he made during his campaign, was simple: The country was enjoying unprecedented prosperity, and he would continue it as president. He also promised to enforce Prohibition, the nationwide ban on alcohol, even though the law was widely ignored by many Americans.

Governor Alfred E. Smith of New York headed the Democratic opposition. Smith, the son of immigrants, was a street-smart New Yorker who wore a derby, smoked a cigar, and had a New York accent. As the first Roman Catholic candidate nominated by a major party, Smith faced many prejudices from voters who were anti-Catholic. Smith's Catholicism and his opposition to Prohibition split the Democratic Party.

The South, which was mainly Protestant and which supported Prohibition, abandoned its traditional Democratic voting pattern. Thus, Hoover, who had never run for political office before, beat Smith with more than 21 million popular votes to Smith's 15 million and an overwhelming 444 electoral votes to Smith's 87.

Herbert Hoover

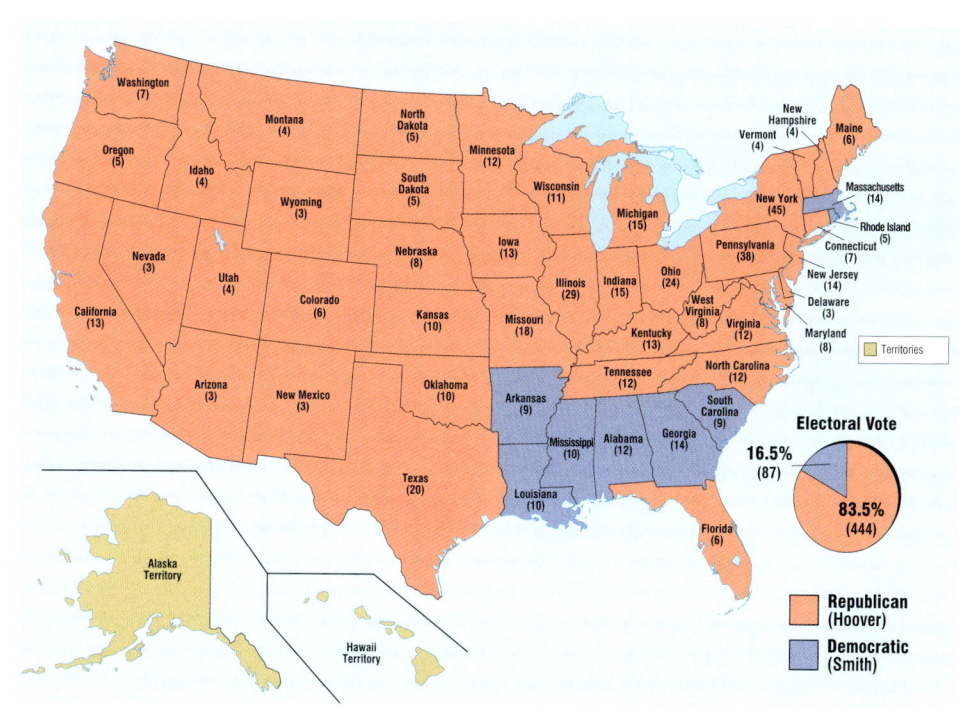

Hoover easily defeated Smith to become president in 1928 by an electoral vote of 444 to 87.

President Hoover

Hoover worked hard to carry out his campaign promises. In June 1929, just three months after his inauguration, he signed a bill that increased aid to American farmers, who had not benefited as much as other groups had from the prosperity of the 1920s. But the promise of his early administration was cut short by events in the autumn of 1929.

On October 29, 1929, the stock market crashed, setting off the worst economic depression in U.S. history. Throughout the 1920s, Americans from all walks of life had invested in the stock market. Most bought shares on margin. That is, they paid only a small percentage of the full price and owed the remainder. When the market collapsed, they not only lost their investment, they owed money.

The crash of the stock market signaled the beginning of a sharp downward spiral in the U.S. economy. Credit tightened, so loans were harder to get. People with cash were reluctant to spend it, and businesses shut down. As businesses closed, more and more people were laid off work. By 1932, banks were failing in large numbers, which led to people losing their hard-earned savings. To make matters even worse, the Midwest experienced a severe drought beginning in 1930.

Hoover's Response to the Depression

President Hoover urged state governments to create jobs through public works, such as government-sponsored projects like building roads and dams. He also encouraged local communities to help the poor, and he urged private charities to help fight poverty as well. Hoover called a meeting of business leaders at the White House in 1929 and urged them not to lay off workers or cut wages.

Herbert Hoover

First Lady Lou Hoover

Lou Henry was born in Iowa in 1874, the only child of Charles and Florence Henry. When she was ten, the family moved to California.

In 1894, Lou entered Stanford University, where she was the only female geology major. While there, Lou became friendly with another student, Herbert Hoover. Hoover later said that he was immediately attracted to Lou's "grinnish smile." The two became engaged and were married in 1899. That same day, they left for China and an adventurous life abroad.

In the early years of their marriage, the Hoovers traveled all over the world. Their two sons, Herbert and Allan, were born overseas. Lou became fluent in five languages.

In 1921, the family moved to Washington, D.C., when Herbert received the appointment as secretary of commerce.

In 1929, the Hoovers moved into the White House. As First Lady, Lou established a reputation as a poised hostess and a giver of elegant dinner parties. As the Depression worsened, the Hoovers used their own money to pay for social events. Lou believed that it was important for the president and First Lady to keep up appearances despite the crisis.

In retirement, the Hoovers divided their time between Palo Alto, California and New York City. Lou Hoover died in New York in January 1944, at the age of 69.

Mrs. Hoover, Allan & Herbert, Jr.

But at first, Hoover did not believe that the federal government could do much to help with the crisis. Direct assistance from the federal government to the nation's poor and unemployed, he believed, would weaken an individual's desire to work. It was the responsibility of private charity and state and local governments, Hoover thought, to help people hurt by the Depression.

Herbert Hoover

A farmer and his sons seek shelter in the midst of a dust storm in Cimarron County, Oklahoma.

The Great Depression continued to worsen. By the end of 1932, more than 25 percent of the workforce, some 13 million people, were unemployed. Every large city (and many other areas) had its shantytown, usually called "Hooverville." These were collections of wooden and paper shacks where the homeless and unemployed lived. To have such places named after him was a source of great anguish for a man who had made his reputation relieving the suffering of starving people.

Hoover, however, was his own worst enemy. He was a poor public speaker who came across as gloomy and pessimistic. Hoover did not inspire people. And at this grave time, the country needed a president who could inspire.

As the economy deteriorated further, the president finally took bolder action. The Emergency Relief Act of 1932 created the Reconstruction Finance Corporation (RFC), a government body that would make loans to banks and businesses and to the states for relief efforts.

The final blow to Hoover's reputation as a leader came in the summer of 1932, when he ordered the army to clear a shantytown set up by the Bonus Army in the center of Washington, D.C. The Bonus Army was a group of World War I veterans who had come to the capital to demand payment of a cash bonus that they believed the government owed them.

Hoover had no intention of paying the bonus, and he also insisted on the dismantling of the Bonus Army shantytown. The U.S. Army came in to storm the shacks. They drove the Bonus Army out of Washington, and the shacks were burned to the ground in a spectacular midnight raid.

Words to Know

Reconstruction Finance Corporation (RFC) (ree-kuhn-STRUHKT-shun FYE-nanss kor-puh-RAY-shuhn): A program initiated by President Herbert Hoover that loaned money to banks and states to help them recover from the Great Depression.

Squatters' shacks dot the landscape along the Willamette River in Portland, Oregon.

To most American citizens, the attack by the army on a group of poverty-stricken veterans seemed a heartless and cruel act. Hoover, the savior of Belgium, had come to be seen as a cold man who cared little for ordinary people.

The 1932 Election

The Depression continued to deepen as the 1932 election campaign got underway. The Republicans renominated Hoover and Curtis, but most observers knew what was about to happen. The Democrats, sensing victory, nominated Governor Franklin D. Roosevelt of New York for president. Roosevelt was the exact opposite of Hoover. His warm and friendly smile, his smooth speaking voice, and his spirit of optimism inspired voters as few presidential candidates ever before or since.

On Election Day, the exhausted president returned to his home in Palo Alto, California, to await the verdict of the American people. It soon became clear that Roosevelt had won a huge victory. That evening, as Hoover read the returns, he received an unsigned telegram. It read: "Vote for Roosevelt and make it unanimous."

After the White House

On the morning of March 4, 1933, his last day in office, President Hoover said, "We are at the end of our strength. There is nothing more we can do." Retiring to his home in California, Hoover remained silent for the next two years. Then he began to criticize Roosevelt in writing and in speeches.

As long as Franklin Roosevelt remained president, Hoover had little opportunity to engage in public service. But after Roosevelt's death, Harry S. Truman, Roosevelt's successor, called on Hoover to help organize food relief for Europe and Asia following World War II.

In 1947, Truman appointed Hoover the head of a commission to recommend reorganization of federal departments. Hoover was profoundly grateful to Truman for giving him the opportunity to contribute his talents once again.

"Brother, Can You Spare a Dime?"

A popular song during the Depression had the line "Brother, can you spare a dime?" A reference to the many people who had been reduced to begging, it was a vivid symbol of how deep the economic crisis cut into the lives of all Americans.

In New York City's Central Park, a small village of shacks made of boxes and packing crates appeared in the early 1930s. The jobless and the homeless who had nowhere else to turn built it and they named it "Hoover Valley."

Other Hoover Valleys, or "Hoovervilles," appeared across the nation. The children who lived in these shantytowns were especially hard hit. Poor diets and inadequate medical and dental care laid the groundwork for a lifetime of health problems. Malnutrition, rickets, pellagra, and other diet-related illnesses were common. And by 1933, the school year had to be shortened because of the loss of tax revenues, leaving children with reduced educational opportunities.

Veterans and their families journeyed to Washington, D.C., in the summer of 1932 seeking early payment of the Soldiers' Bonus Act.

During the 1950s, Hoover, now in his eighties, assumed the role of elder statesman and adviser to presidents. The memory of the Depression and his presidency had faded. There was now the perception that the former president was an honorable and decent person who had done his best to help the country during an extraordinarily trying period in its history.

In his final years, Hoover lived in the Waldorf-Astoria Hotel in New York City. He died there on October 20, 1964, at the age of 90. Two years before, the Herbert Hoover Presidential Library had been dedicated in West Branch, Iowa. It was on its grounds that his body and the remains of Mrs. Hoover, who had died in 1944, were buried.

Hoover is greeted by Polish war orphans during his 1946 visit to Warsaw.

Franklin D. Roosevelt

Franklin Delano Roosevelt served as president during the two greatest crises of the twentieth century: the Great Depression and World War II. He was an inspiring leader so admired by the people that they elected him president four times, more than any person in American History.

Despite the challenges that he faced in office, Roosevelt loved being president. Few Americans knew that their beloved "FDR" who was so strong and full of hope, could not walk unaided. The victim of an attack of polio when he was 39 years old, Roosevelt was a paraplegic (partially paralyzed). His recovery from this devastating illness and his rise to the presidency is one of the most inspiring stories in American political history.

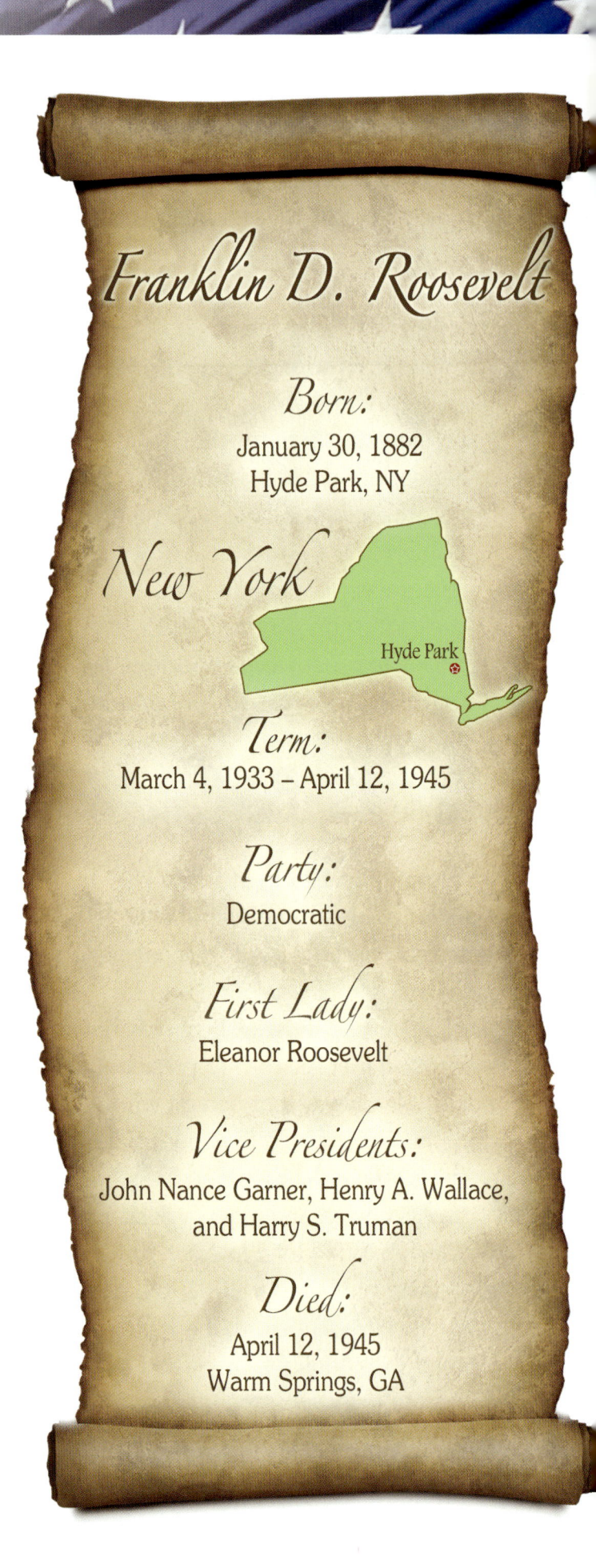

Vice President John Nance Garner

Franklin D. Roosevelt

Born:
January 30, 1882
Hyde Park, NY

New York
Hyde Park

Term:
March 4, 1933 – April 12, 1945

Party:
Democratic

First Lady:
Eleanor Roosevelt

Vice Presidents:
John Nance Garner, Henry A. Wallace, and Harry S. Truman

Died:
April 12, 1945
Warm Springs, GA

Franklin D. Roosevelt

32nd President of the United States

Franklin D. Roosevelt

Early Life

Roosevelt was born in Hyde Park, New York, on January 30, 1882, the only child of James and Sara Delano Roosevelt. His parents were wealthy members of an elite group of old New York families who lived on big estates along the Hudson River. Young Franklin was a treasured child who grew up surrounded by servants and governesses. Except for one brief period, he received tutoring at home until he was 14 years old. Then, he entered Groton, a boarding school for wealthy young men. After graduating from Groton in 1900, Franklin entered Harvard, from which he graduated in 1904. He then went on to study law at Columbia University Law School. While still at Harvard, Franklin fell in love with a distant cousin, Eleanor Roosevelt. Franklin and Eleanor were married in March, 1905. The bride's uncle, President Theodore Roosevelt, gave her away at the wedding.

Franklin Roosevelt, 1913

Early Career in Politics

Franklin began practicing law in New York City, but his mind was set on a political career. In 1910, he had the opportunity to run for the New York state senate as a Democrat. He won the election and quickly allied himself with the reform wing of the party.

In 1912, Roosevelt campaigned vigorously for the Democratic presidential nominee, Governor Woodrow Wilson of New Jersey. After Wilson's victory in the election, Roosevelt was rewarded with the job of assistant secretary of the navy. It was the very job Theodore Roosevelt held as he began his rise to the White House.

Franklin Roosevelt loved being in Washington, D.C. He was young, ambitious, and intelligent, and he took over the day-to-day management of the Navy Department with vigor. He worked tirelessly to make sure that the navy was prepared for any conflict. When the United States entered World War I in 1917, Roosevelt supervised the preparation of the navy for wartime activity.

Franklin D. Roosevelt

Ohio Governor James M. Cox and Franklin D. Roosevelt of New York arrive at the White House for a conference with the president.

At the 1920 National Democratic Convention, they chose Governor James Cox of Ohio as the presidential candidate. The convention then turned to Roosevelt for the vice-presidential slot. Roosevelt ran a strenuous campaign, traveling across the country by train and making more than 1,000 speeches. He knew that the Democrats would be defeated in the 1920 election, but he welcomed the opportunity to campaign and make a good name for himself as a future candidate.

The Democrats were overwhelmingly defeated in 1920 by the Republican ticket, headed by Warren G. Harding. After Harding was sworn in, on March 4, 1921, there were few jobs for Democrats in Washington, D.C., so Roosevelt took a break from politics.

Polio

In August 1921, Roosevelt was vacationing at his family's summer home on Campobello Island, New Brunswick, in Canada. After a strenuous day of sailing, fishing, and jogging, he suddenly became sick, with a high fever and loss of feeling in his legs. When doctors finally diagnosed the illness, the news was devastating: Roosevelt was suffering from infantile paralysis, the dreaded disease also known as polio. He would never walk unaided again.

The political career of the 39-year-old Roosevelt now seemed to be over. Everyone believed that a man in a wheelchair could never be elected to high political office. Sara Roosevelt wanted her son to return to Hyde Park, where she could take care of him.

But Eleanor fought for her husband. She told her mother-in-law that Franklin would not live the rest of his life as an invalid. She also encouraged Franklin to believe that he would return one day to politics and that his disability would in no way prevent him from holding public office.

Sara and Eleanor fought over Franklin's future, but in the end, Eleanor won, with the help of Franklin, who also fervently believed that he would one day walk again. He never did regain the full use of his legs, but he never stopped believing that he would. This belief sustained him for the rest of his life.

Franklin D. Roosevelt

Franklin and Eleanor Roosevelt relax with their son, Elliot, and his wife in Warm Springs, Georgia.

Warm Springs

Roosevelt soon became interested in helping others who suffered from polio. Using his personal fortune, he bought a former resort and 2,600 acres of land in the piney woods of western Georgia, near a spring whose warm waters supposedly had medicinal effects. Here, in 1927, Roosevelt established the Georgia Warm Springs Foundation for the study and treatment of polio.

Polio victims from all over the country went to Warm Springs, as the site came to be called, where they received treatment and swam in pools heated by the almost 90 degree mineral waters.

"Rosey," as Franklin was affectionately called by the other patients, spent many months of the year at Warm Springs, where the climate, treatment, and companionship did much to help his recovery. During times of stress in later years, he always returned to Warm Springs, where he kept a small cottage on the grounds of the treatment facility.

Governor of New York

Before he could return to politics, Roosevelt wanted to walk as best he could. Walking without assistance, however, was no longer possible. Instead, with the aid of heavy steel braces, a cane, and leaning on the arm of one of his grown sons, he learned to thrust his legs forward by swinging his hips. It was a stiff and awkward walk that could be done for only a few steps. But it was good enough. Roosevelt appeared to be walking, and that was the image that he wanted the public to see.

In 1924, Roosevelt stood at the podium at the Democratic Convention and nominated Governor Alfred E. Smith of New York for the presidency. It was his official return to politics. Four years later, FDR again gave the nominating speech for Alfred Smith at the 1928 Convention. Smith was now leaving the governorship of New York to run for the White House. He convinced Roosevelt to run for governor, and Roosevelt felt that he was strong enough to return to elected office.

The year 1928 was another Republican year, however. Herbert Hoover overwhelmed Smith for the presidency. Roosevelt, though, narrowly won the election for governor of New York.

When the stock market crashed in 1929 and the country slid into a depression, Governor Roosevelt faced the crisis with innovative and dynamic programs. He created the Temporary Emergency Relief Administration to aid the unemployed, and he reduced the work week for women and children.

He convinced the New York legislature to pass a program of pensions for the elderly. Roosevelt also enacted a program to bring relief to New York's farmers, and he brought public utilities such as gas and electric companies under state regulation to improve services and keep prices down.

After a landslide reelection in 1930, Governor Roosevelt was now prepared to pursue the prize he had wanted all of his political life: the presidency of the United States.

Franklin D. Roosevelt stands at the podium giving a speech.

The 1932 Election

A Democratic victory in 1932 seemed almost inevitable. The Republicans renominated president Herbert Hoover, but his chances for reelection were slim. After some debate, the Democratic Convention nominated Roosevelt for president. Roosevelt chose John Nance Garner of Texas, the speaker of the U.S. House of Representatives, as his vice president.

Addressing the Convention after his nomination, Roosevelt promised a "new deal" for the American people. That term would later become identified with Roosevelt's domestic policies aimed at recovery.

In November 1932, the voters chose Franklin Roosevelt over Hoover. The Electoral College gave the Democrat 472 electoral votes to Hoover's 59. After the assurance of victory, Roosevelt went to the New York City townhouse owned by his mother. Waiting for him at the front door was Sara Roosevelt, who embraced her son and said it was the happiest day of her life. She had always believed in him, but she never expected that after the crippling attack of polio, he would one day be president.

President Roosevelt: The First Hundred Days

Roosevelt was sworn in as president on the steps of the Capitol on the gray, chilly noon of March 4, 1933. More than 100,000 people stood in the plaza below and listened to the new president tell the nation that "the only thing we have to fear is fear itself."

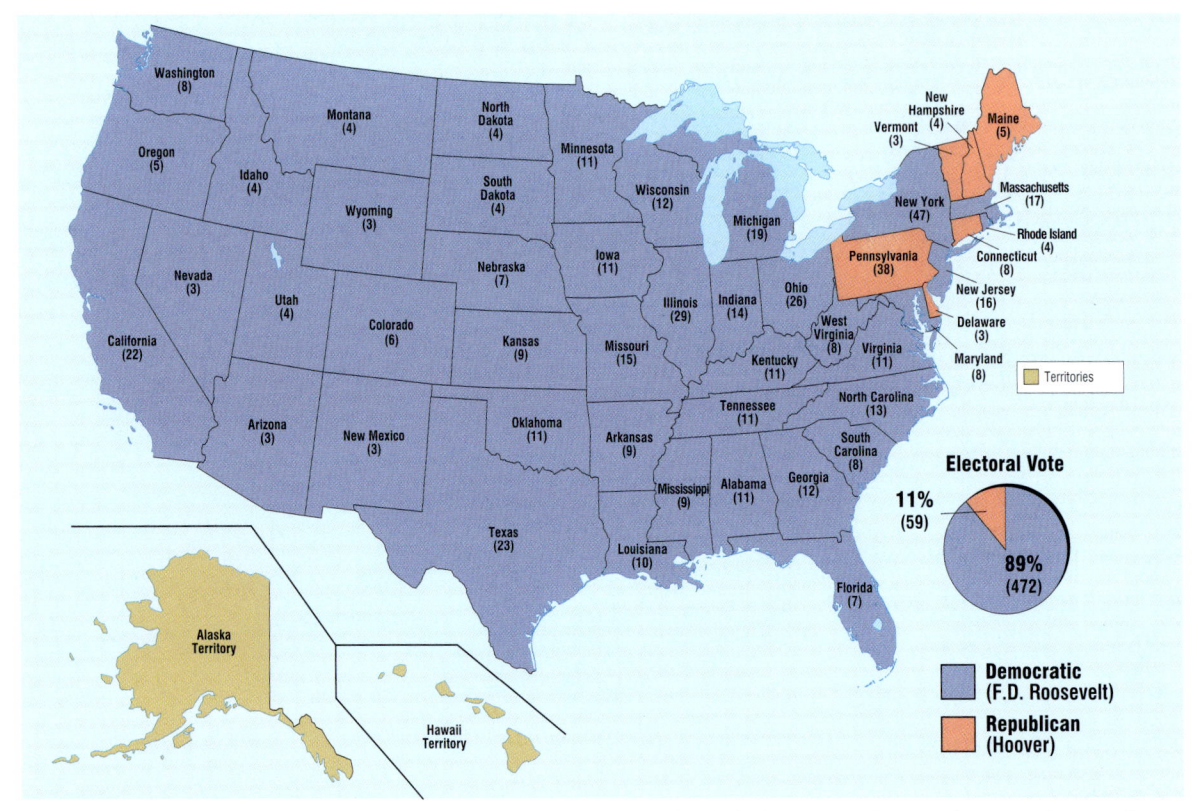

Roosevelt's optimism helped him to win the election of 1932 beating Hoover by an electoral vote of 472 to 59.

Franklin D. Roosevelt

His voice, so full of optimism and confidence, helped steady a nation on the brink of economic collapse. The president immediately closed all the nation's banks for a four-day bank holiday. He asked Americans to have confidence in their banking institutions, and he had auditors go over the books. Those banks declared sound were allowed to reopen. When they did reopen, deposits exceeded withdrawals. Roosevelt had helped restore confidence in the nation's financial institutions.

Over the next 100 days, Congress passed a torrent of legislation. They created the National Recovery Administration (NRA) to encourage industry and labor to set fair prices and wages. They developed the Civilian Conservation Corps (CCC) to create jobs for young men and women helping to restore forests. They enacted the Agricultural Adjustment Act (AAA) to create a system of price supports for farmers and to help hard-pressed agriculture recover from the effects of the Depression.

To relieve unemployment, the government created the Works Progress Administration (WPA). Over the next seven years, the WPA would build public buildings, bridges, dams, and housing and provide work for millions of people.

Roosevelt explained his policies using the new medium of radio. Through what were called "fireside chats," the president told the radio audience what was happening and what they could expect in the future. The American people felt that the president was in their living rooms, by the fireside, talking to them personally.

Franklin D. Roosevelt delivers a fireside chat in Washington, D.C.

Words to Know

New Deal (NOO DEEL): The huge domestic economic-recovery program of President Franklin D. Roosevelt.

Electoral College (i-LEK-tor-uhl KOL-ij): The group that formally elects the president and vice president by casting electoral votes. Members of the Electoral College are elected by popular vote—the vote of the people—in each state.

National Recovery Administration (NASH-uh-nuhl ree-KOV-er-ee ad-min-uh-STRAY-shun): A New Deal program that encouraged labor and industry to set fair prices and wages.

Civilian Conservation Corps (CCC) (si-VIL-yuhn kon-sur-VAY-shun KOR): A New Deal program that created government jobs for people to work restoring the nation's forests.

Agricultural Adjustment Act (AAA) (AG-ruh-kul-chur-uhl uh-JUHST-muhnt AKT): A New Deal program to help the nation's farmers.

Franklin D. Roosevelt

First Lady Eleanor Roosevelt

Anna Eleanor Roosevelt was born in New York City in 1884, the daughter of Elliott and Anna Hall Roosevelt. Her father was the younger brother of President Theodore Roosevelt. She was nicknamed "Little Nell" by her father and known by her middle name for most of her life.

Eleanor was a shy and awkward child who suffered much loss in her early years. When she was eight, her mother died of diphtheria. Her father, who suffered from alcoholism and severe emotional problems, was unable to care for Eleanor and her younger brother, Hall. As a result, the children went to live with Grandmother Hall after their mother's death. Less than two years later, Elliott Roosevelt died, leaving Eleanor an orphan at nine.

The Roosevelts were a wealthy family, and in her teens, they sent Eleanor to England to a private boarding school. There she developed more self-confidence and grew into an attractive young woman.

After completing school in England, Eleanor returned to the United States, where she soon met a distant cousin with the same last name: Franklin Delano Roosevelt. Although still shy, Eleanor was a serious and striking person; she was thin, graceful, and nearly six feet tall.

The fun-loving Franklin was immediately attracted to her, and she, in turn, was attracted to the handsome and charming young man. They were engaged in 1903. After overcoming the objections of Franklin's mother, they were married in 1905.

Franklin and Eleanor had six children. A young son died in infancy, but a daughter and four sons survived into adulthood. During these years, as Franklin's political career blossomed, Eleanor raised her family and performed the social duties of a political wife.

Franklin's attack of polio in 1921 was a turning point in Eleanor's life. She was determined to help him return to politics someday. In the meantime, she decided to be his eyes and ears: Since he could not participate in politics, she would stand

---

Other important New Deal measures also passed after the first 100 days. In 1933, the Tennessee Valley Authority (TVA) was created. This is the first time that the federal government took a direct role in a local development plan. The TVA created dams and brought irrigation and electricity to the Tennessee Valley region.

Another important bill was the Social Security Act, providing government

in for him. She joined the women's division of the New York state Democratic Party, where she developed important political connections. She also began her lifelong interest in social causes, especially the rights of women and the improvement of conditions for African Americans and children.

By the time Eleanor Roosevelt became First Lady in 1933, she had carved out a life of her own as a political figure. She also understood social conditions better than any of her predecessors had. Eleanor accepted the social responsibilities of First Lady, although she hated small talk and preferred dealing with real issues.

At the same time, she broke precedents by holding her own press conferences, by traveling to all parts of the country and reporting back to the president on what she had seen, and by writing a daily newspaper column called, "My Day."

Eleanor and Franklin considered themselves a team: He was president, but since he could not get around easily because of his partial paralysis, she was his ambassador to the country and the world. During the war, Eleanor traveled to England and later the Pacific, where she visited wounded soldiers and the troops on the front lines.

When the president died in 1945, Eleanor returned to her cottage, Val-Kill, on the grounds of the Roosevelt estate in Hyde Park. Within a year, however, President Truman named her to a position at the United Nations. For the rest of her life, Eleanor remained involved with the United Nations and with humanitarian and peace causes. She also remained active in the Democratic Party.

Eleanor Roosevelt's energies faded only in the last year of her life. When she died in New York in 1962, at the age of 78, people genuinely mourned her loss and remembered her as a great world figure.

By her broad interests and activism, Eleanor Roosevelt forever transformed the role of First Lady. She brought the position out of its narrow social sphere and made it acceptable for the First Lady to have a life of her own and to be a public figure with public interests. Most scholars regard her as the greatest First Lady in history.

retirement pensions for people over age 65. Today Social Security is a vast program available to all Americans receiving funding through payroll taxes deducted from workers' paychecks.

Words to Know

Social Security Act (SOH-shuhl si-KYOOR-i-tee AKT): A bill establishing government sponsored pensions for older Americans. It was passed in 1935.

The New Deal Under Attack

In 1935, the New Deal began to come under serious attack. Opponents of the president challenged the constitutionality of much legislation in the courts. And in 1935, they began to score some important victories. In May 1935, the U.S. Supreme Court declared that the National Recovery Administration was unconstitutional.

The case Schechter Poultry Corporation v. the United States stated that the NRA improperly gave powers of the legislative branch to the executive branch of government. The following year, significant portions of the Agricultural Adjustment Act were also declared unconstitutional.

To Roosevelt and the Democrats, it looked like the Supreme Court, consisting of nine justices all appointed by Republican presidents, would strike down the entire New Deal. It was 1936, an election year, and Roosevelt took his case to the people. Stating that "I am the issue," Roosevelt declared that "you are either for me or against me."

On Election Day, the electorate spoke. They returned Roosevelt for a second term by the largest winning margin in history. Roosevelt won 523 electoral votes over the 8 electoral votes won by the Republican presidential candidate, Governor Alfred Landon of Kansas. Flushed with victory, the president decided to move against the Supreme Court.

Roosevelt's Second Term

As he began his second term, early in 1937, President Roosevelt was afraid that the Court was about to declare the Social Security Act unconstitutional. He also wanted some revenge against the Court, which had ruined so many New Deal programs.

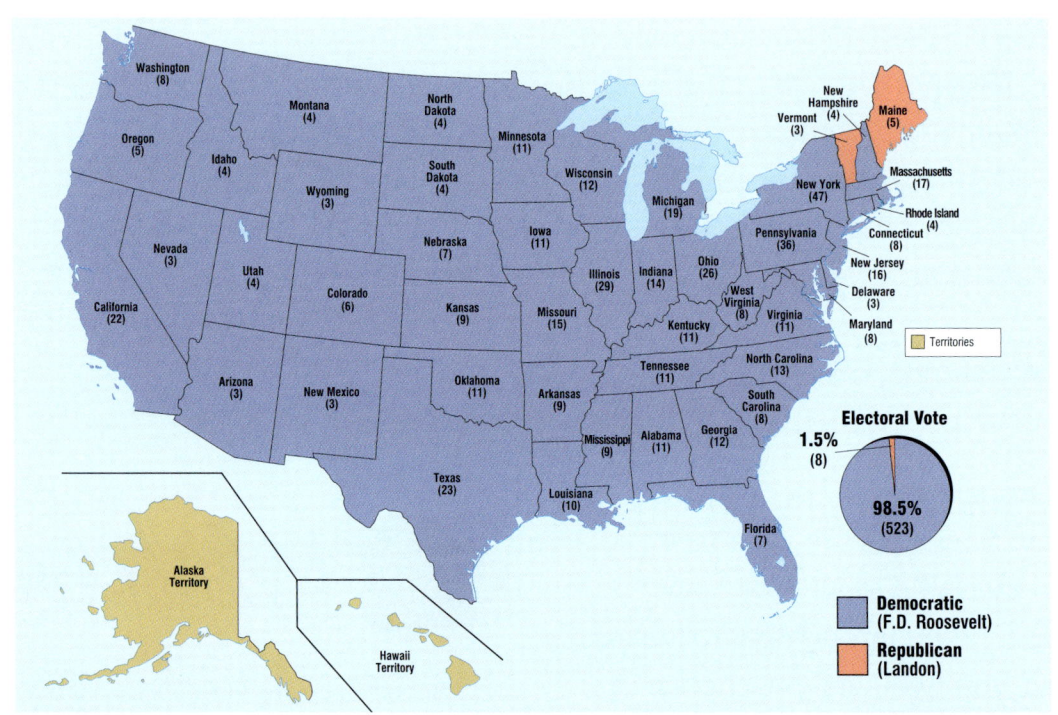

Although battling Congress to continue the New Deal policies, the people spoke clearly in support of Roosevelt to help him win reelection in 1936 with an electoral vote of 523 to Landon's 8.

MORE SECURITY FOR THE AMERICAN FAMILY

WHEN AN INSURED WORKER DIES, LEAVING DEPENDENT CHILDREN AND A WIDOW, BOTH MOTHER AND CHILDREN RECEIVE MONTHLY BENEFITS UNTIL THE LATTER REACH 18.

FOR INFORMATION WRITE OR CALL AT THE NEAREST FIELD OFFICE OF THE **SOCIAL SECURITY BOARD**

An early poster explains one aspect of Social Security benefits.

Roosevelt devised a plan to create a friendlier Court, one that would be more open to his policies. He proposed legislation that would give the president the power to appoint an additional justice for any justice who was over age 70, to a maximum of 15 people on the Court. Since most of the justices were in their seventies, the bill would have given Roosevelt the authority to appoint at least six new ones. Presumably, the new ones would be friendly to his New Deal.

Opponents called Roosevelt's plan an attempt at "Court packing." The proposal proved to be much more controversial than Roosevelt had anticipated. Even some Democrats feared that the president was trying to alter the balance of power between the branches of government.

Roosevelt used all of his famous charm to convince wavering Democrats to support his plan. In the end, however, the Congress refused to pass the president's full plan to reorganize the Supreme Court.

The loss was a devastating defeat for Roosevelt. It proved that he could be beaten, even in a Congress controlled by Democrats. The reforming energy of the New Deal seemed to be running out of steam. Nevertheless, the controversy and the threat of reorganization apparently sent a message to the Court.

It declared the Social Security Act constitutional. And Congress had passed the Supreme Court Retirement Act, allowing judges to retire at 70. Within the next four years, seven elderly justices did retire, opening appointments for Roosevelt to fill with his own justices.

Threats from Abroad

By the late 1930s, Roosevelt's attention refocused from domestic affairs to the growing problems overseas. In Europe, the German dictator Adolf Hitler was re-arming Germany and threatening neighboring countries. Added to the danger in Europe was the threat of Japanese expansion in the Pacific region. In 1937, Japan invaded China and was poised to menace other nations of Asia.

Franklin D. Roosevelt

Adolf Hitler was the leader of the Nazi Party in Germany. The symbol on his armband is called a swastika.

Roosevelt perceived the policies of Germany and Japan as a direct threat to the security of the United States. He understood that the United States was no longer secure simply because the vast Atlantic and Pacific Oceans bordered it. In the modern age of airplanes and big navies, a threat in Europe or the Pacific could quickly become a threat to the United States.

Unfortunately for Roosevelt, the American people did not agree. An overwhelming majority of the population was isolationist. That is, they believed that the United States needed to avoid involvement in any foreign disputes or wars. As a result, the president was forced to proceed cautiously in international affairs, not straying too far from the wishes of the American people, but defending the United States as best he could.

In 1939, Germany invaded Poland, and World War II in Europe began. England and France went to war against Germany, but for the time being, the United States declared its neutrality. In 1940, Germany invaded France and defeated and occupied that nation in a few short weeks. England now faced Germany on its own, and seemed close to being bombed into surrender.

Roosevelt was determined not to let the British be defeated. But Congress had prohibited him from giving any weapons to the British unless they paid for them in cash. The British, however, were already bankrupt from the cost of war. They could not afford to pay cash for the weapons they needed to defend themselves against German attack.

Franklin D. Roosevelt

To get around Congress, Roosevelt devised an ingenious plan called "Lend Lease." The United States would lend the tanks, planes, and guns that the British needed. After the war, the British would return the weapons to the United States. It would be like lending a neighbor a garden hose to put out a fire, Roosevelt said. Once the fire was out, the neighbor would return the hose. Through this plan, Roosevelt was able to get huge shipments of arms to the British in their darkest hour. Later, Lend Lease was also extended to the Soviet Union and other Allied Forces.

A Third Term

By 1940, Roosevelt had been president for seven years. He looked forward to retiring to Hyde Park at the end of his second term, but he was torn by a sense of duty to continue serving during a time of grave crisis. To do so, however, he would have to challenge a sacred tradition in American politics established by George Washington: No president had ever served more than two terms.

Roosevelt decided to challenge tradition and run for a third term. The Democratic Party was overjoyed and relieved that its greatest vote-getter would once again head the ticket. However, Vice President Jon Nance Garner decided to retire. Roosevelt chose Secretary of Agriculture Henry Wallace to be the new vice-presidential candidate.

The Republicans chose a little-known businessman, Wendell L. Willkie, as their presidential nominee. Willkie turned out to be a strong and appealing candidate. Although he did not support many New Deal measures, he was a moderate who had wide popularity. Still, the Roosevelt magnetism won out in the end. Willkie received more than 22 million popular votes to the president's more than 27 million, but he won only 82 electoral votes to Roosevelt's 449.

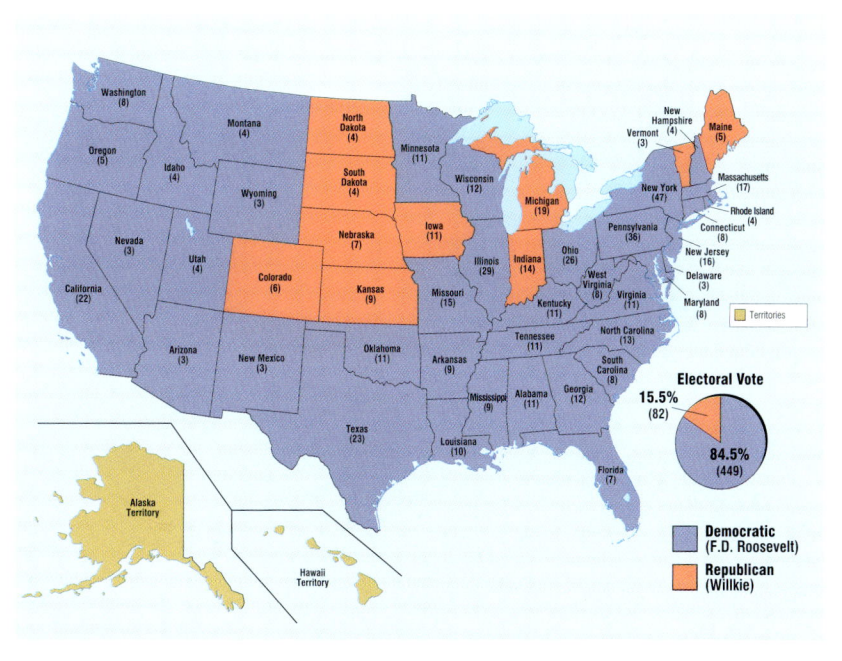

Roosevelt won an unprecedented third term in office in 1940, defeating Willkie with an electoral vote of 449 to 82.

Words to Know

Lend Lease (LEND LEESS): A U.S. program enacted in March 1941 that lent weapons to the British, and later other Allies, in the struggle against Germany.

America Enters the War

As Roosevelt began his third term in 1941, the war clouds over Europe and the Pacific darkened. Germany continued its brutal bombing of England, while its armies turned eastward to invade the Balkans and Russia. In the Pacific, Japan and the United States continued to negotiate their differences, but the outlook for peace seemed to diminish with each passing month.

The American people remained strongly isolationist. Roosevelt, however, felt that American involvement was unavoidable. He believed that the Germans would provoke an incident in the Atlantic that would outrage the American people and free him to ask Congress for a declaration of war.

Roosevelt was right about an incident, but he was wrong about the ocean. On December 7, 1941, hundreds of Japanese planes staged an early morning surprise attack on the U.S. naval base at Pearl Harbor, Hawaii, sinking ships, wrecking docks and buildings, and killing more than 2,000 Americans.

A small boat rescues a seaman from the USS West Virginia after the Japanese attack on Pearl Harbor, Hawaii.

Franklin D. Roosevelt

The following day, Roosevelt appeared before Congress. Calling December 7 "the day that shall live in infamy," he asked for a declaration of war against Japan. Three days later, Germany and Italy declared war on the United States, which declared war in return. The American people rallied behind their president. America was now in World War II.

President Roosevelt signs the declaration of war against Germany, December 11, 1941.

War Leader

From 1942 on, Roosevelt spent all his time leading Britain, France, the United States, and the Soviet Union, against Germany, Italy, and Japan. The United States had to go from a peacetime nation to a war footing very quickly. Private industries converted to industries producing military supplies. The automobile industry, for example, switched many of its factories to producing tanks and trucks for the army. Clothing manufacturers began to make uniforms.

As men went to war, women filled their positions in industry and agriculture. A

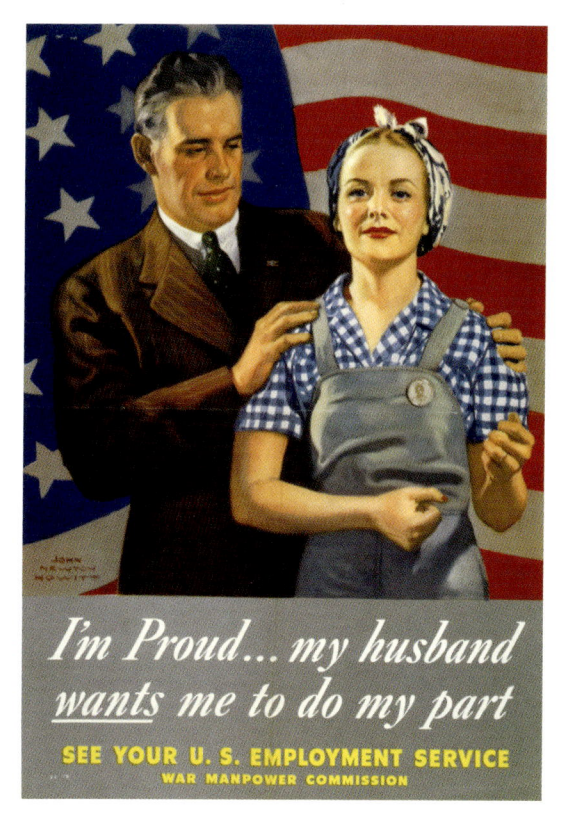

A wartime poster by John Newton shows a husband, in business suit, and wife, in working clothes, standing in front of a U.S. flag.

fictional character named "Rosie the Riveter" became famous, representing the millions of women who took jobs to help support their families and keep factories running.

During the war, Roosevelt traveled overseas for a number of meetings with Allied leaders. In January 1943, he journeyed to Casablanca to meet British Prime Minister Winston Churchill; and later in 1943, he traveled to Tehran, Iran, where he met Soviet leader Joseph Stalin. The most important conference occurred at Yalta, in the Soviet Union, in February 1945. There Roosevelt, Churchill, and Stalin discussed the postwar political situation in Europe and the fate of the soon-to-be-defeated Germany.

Franklin D. Roosevelt

Throughout the war, Roosevelt called for a postwar world that would be free of war and would respect human rights. He worked tirelessly for the creation of a united nations organization to replace the League of Nations, which had been founded after World War I. The United States, deeply isolationist at the time, had never joined the League. Roosevelt was determined that the United States would be a leading member of the new United Nations.

1944 Election

The year 1944 was an election year, and in July, the president let it be known that he would accept another nomination. He considered it his duty to continue in office as long as the United States was at war. The Democratic Convention agreed, and it selected Senator Harry S. Truman of Missouri to be the new vice-presidential nominee, replacing Henry Wallace.

The Republicans nominated Governor Thomas E. Dewey of New York for the presidency, hoping that the youthful 42-year-old candidate would appeal to the voters. The old Roosevelt magic still worked, however, and in November, the president won a fourth term, gathering 432 electoral votes to Dewey's 99, although the popular vote was very close.

Because of the war, Roosevelt wanted to keep his fourth inauguration as simple as possible. Instead of being sworn in at the Capitol, Roosevelt took the oath of office on the south portico of the White House before a small group of family and spectators. Two days later, he left for Yalta, on what was to be his final trip abroad.

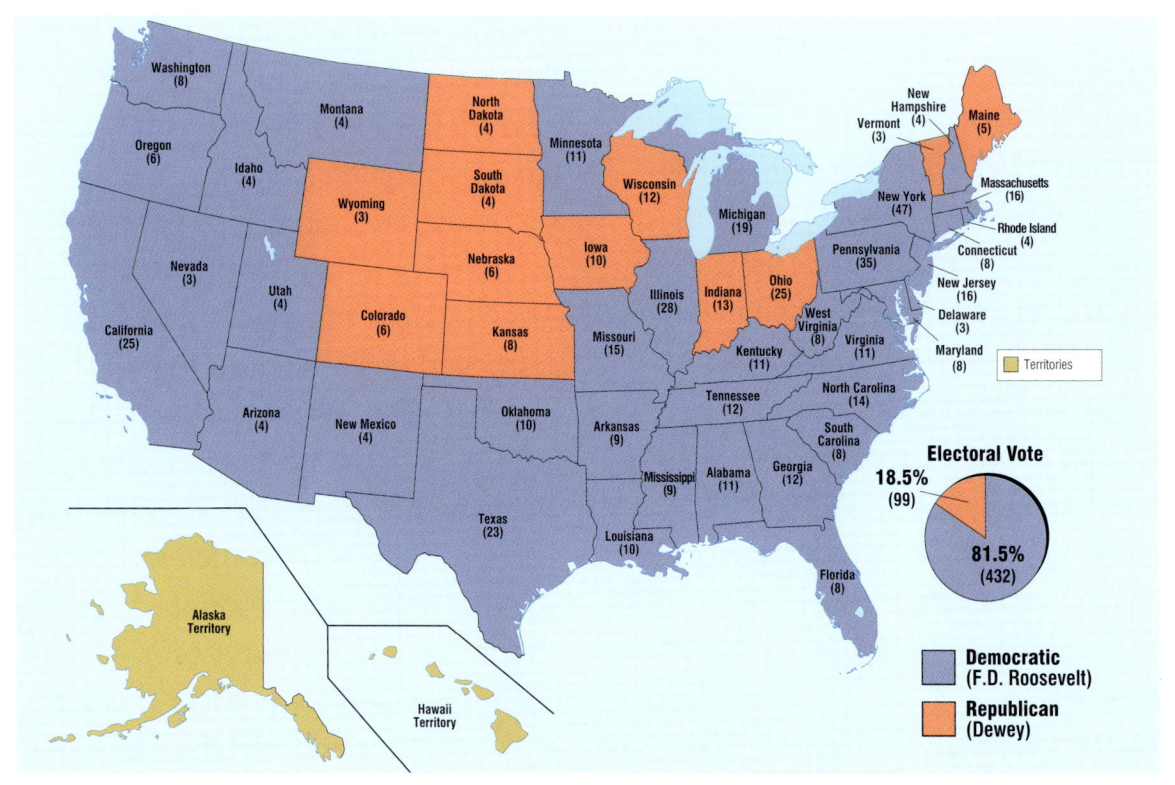

Roosevelt was reelected for his fourth term in office in 1944.

Franklin D. Roosevelt

The Last Months

In the spring of 1944, a number of the president's friends and family members became alarmed at his appearance. He was losing weight and seemed tired most of the time. They convinced him to see a heart specialist and have an examination.

The doctor discovered that the president was seriously ill, suffering from advanced heart disease and high blood pressure. Doctors placed Roosevelt on medication and told him to rest and cut back on his strenuous schedule. The public did not receive information about the seriousness of Roosevelt's illness. In fact, the president himself never asked his doctors what was wrong with him. And since he didn't ask, the doctors didn't tell. Instead, Roosevelt simply took his pills and asked no questions.

Throughout the remainder of 1944, Roosevelt's health deteriorated. His hands shook, and he continued to lose weight. He often dozed off at meetings. After returning from Yalta, the president began a lengthy vacation at his cottage at Warm Springs, Georgia. He hoped that the country air and the familiar surroundings of Warm Springs would revive him.

About 1:00 P.M. on April 12, 1945, Roosevelt was sitting in the living room of the cottage having his portrait sketched. Suddenly, he rubbed his forehead and said, "I have a terrific headache." He collapsed and fell into a deep coma. Two and a half hours later, he was pronounced dead of a cerebral hemorrhage.

For a nation that had known no other president for half a generation, Roosevelt's death was an overwhelming shock. The U.S. Army was poised for its final victory in Germany, and in the Pacific, American bombers were savaging the Japanese mainland in preparation for the final attack on that country.

Roosevelt, the man who had led his nation through depression and war, never lived to see the end of the conflict. Like another great president, Abraham Lincoln, he was taken at the moment of victory.

Franklin D. Roosevelt and Eleanor Roosevelt gather for a photograph with their 13 grandchildren in Washington, D.C.

Harry S. Truman

Harry Truman never wanted to be president, but he was catapulted into the White House by the death of Franklin Roosevelt. It was a critical time in American history. Although Germany was close to surrender, there was still a potentially bloody and long war with Japan ahead.

Shortly after he became president, Truman was told of a secret weapon being developed in the deserts of New Mexico: an atomic bomb, more powerful than any bomb ever known. Within a few months, Truman had to decide whether or not to use this weapon of mass destruction in order to end the war with Japan.

Truman's presidency began in the final days of war and extended into the early 1950s. His foreign and domestic policies shaped the postwar world for 40 years. Today, many regard Truman as one of the country's most important presidents.

Vice President Alben W. Barkley

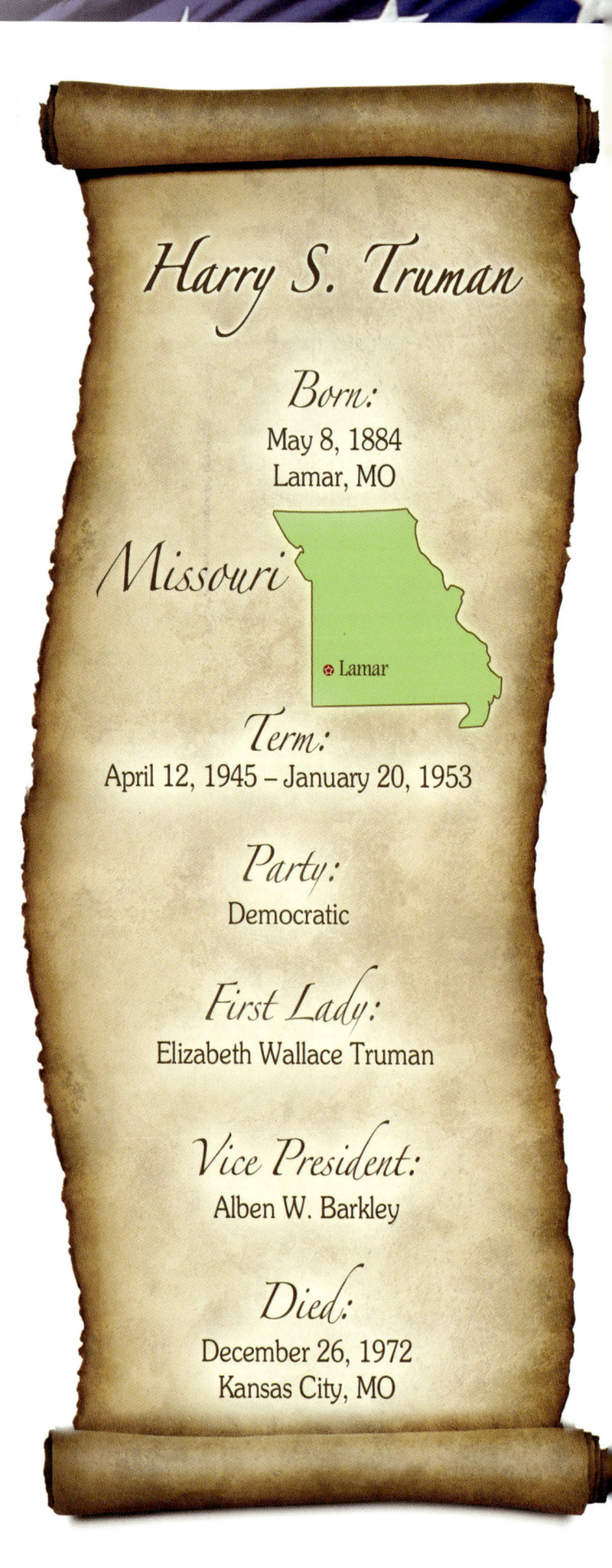

Harry S. Truman

Born:
May 8, 1884
Lamar, MO

Missouri
Lamar

Term:
April 12, 1945 – January 20, 1953

Party:
Democratic

First Lady:
Elizabeth Wallace Truman

Vice President:
Alben W. Barkley

Died:
December 26, 1972
Kansas City, MO

Harry S. Truman

33rd President of the United States

Early Life

Harry S. Truman was born in Lamar, Missouri, on May 8, 1884. He was the son of John Anderson Truman, a farmer and cattle trader, and Martha Young Truman. They gave him the middle initial "S" only, but no name, in honor of his grandfathers Anderson Shippe Truman and Solomon Young.

In 1890, the family moved to Independence, Missouri, near Kansas City. Harry loved to read. He often spent hours at a time in the library at Independence. There, he read everything he could about American history.

After finishing high school in 1901, Harry applied for a commission to the military academy at West Point, but they rejected him because of his poor eyesight. He did not have enough money to pay college tuition, so he took a job as a mailroom clerk at the Kansas City Star. He also joined the Missouri National Guard; he was a member from 1905 to 1911. After five years in Kansas City, Truman decided that he had enough of city life. He returned to work on his father's farm.

Military Service and Marriage

In 1917, the United States entered World War I. Truman, now 33 years old, rejoined the National Guard and so was called to active military duty. In March 1918, his unit was sent to France, where Truman saw action in several battles.

Harry and Bess Truman pause for a backyard wedding photo on June 28, 1919.

After the war ended in 1918, Truman returned to Independence. In 1919, he married his childhood sweetheart, Elizabeth "Bess" Wallace. Then, Truman tried his hand at business. With a friend, he invested all of his savings in a haberdashery (clothing) store. The business failed two years later. Its demise had far reaching consequences for Truman, and ultimately, for the United States. Discouraged by business, Truman decided to look for a job in politics.

Harry S. Truman

"Truman for Senator" Campaign Headquarters

Senator Truman

Through an old army friend, Harry Truman received an appointment as overseer of highways for Jackson County, Missouri. He decided to try for a higher elective position, and in 1926, he was elected presiding judge of Jackson County. Despite the title "judge," the position was really that of a country administrator responsible for the country highway and building construction projects.

In an era when there was much corruption in local politics in Missouri, Truman soon earned a reputation as an honest politician. He seemed destined for higher office. In 1934, Truman entered the Democratic Party primary for a seat in the U.S. Senate from Missouri. He defeated three other candidates and went on to win the election. The unsuccessful store owner was now a senator.

In the Senate, Truman was a big supporter of Roosevelt's New Deal policies. However, he did not make a strong reputation for himself until after his reelection as senator in 1940. When the United States entered World War II in 1941, Truman became concerned about waste in federal spending. The war was creating whole new areas of federal spending, and Truman wanted to make sure that the nation's money was not being wasted.

After touring the country at his own expense to inspect factories and defense facilities, Truman asked the Senate to establish the Special Committee to Investigate the National Defense Program. The "Truman Committee," as it soon was called, helped root out much mismanagement, waste, and negligence in the defense industry. It saved the government some 15 billion dollars during the war years and brought fame to Truman.

Vice President for 82 Days

With World War II entering its final phase, in 1944, President Roosevelt decided to run for a fourth term. Vice president Henry Wallace, who had been elected in 1940, wanted to run again, but many people in the party who felt that he was too radical opposed him. The party considered many names, but eventually the president agreed to Truman as a compromise.

At first, Truman flatly refused to take the nomination. He loved being in the Senate, and he did not want to leave it for the somewhat powerless office of vice president. Party leaders persuaded him that it was his duty to become vice president. Reluctantly, Truman accepted. He won the election with Roosevelt in November 1944 and was sworn in at the White House on January 20, 1945.

On the afternoon of April 12, 1945, Truman was enjoying a drink in a Senate office with a few colleagues. As he chatted and laughed with his friends, someone handed him a telephone message. In it, he was asked to come to the White House immediately. Truman, fearing the worst, rushed to the executive mansion, where Mrs. Roosevelt greeted him. Gently, she informed him that the president had died earlier that afternoon in Warm Springs, Georgia.

That evening, Harry Truman took the oath of office as the 33rd president of the United States in the cabinet room of the White House. He told newspaper reporters that he felt that "the moon, the stars, and all the planets had fallen upon me."

President Truman: Ending the War

When Truman became president, some fighting was still going on in Germany, and the war against Japan was far from over. Two weeks after he became president, Truman was told about the top-secret atomic bomb project in New Mexico. A few days later, on May 7, 1945, the fighting ended in Europe as Germany surrendered. Truman proclaimed the next day V-E (Victory in Europe) Day.

In the Pacific, the United States was heavily bombing Japanese cities, but most people believed that the Japanese would never surrender. An invasion of Japan, therefore, could potentially result in millions of casualties.

Truman announces the end of World War II.

Harry S. Truman

Churchill, Stalin, and Truman shake hands at the Potsdam Conference.

Truman had to decide whether to use the atomic bomb on Japan, in the hope that this weapon would shock the Japanese government into a quick surrender. Before making the decision, Truman journeyed to Potsdam, Germany, in July 1945, to meet with Prime Minister Winston Churchill of Great Britain and Soviet leader Joseph Stalin. At the Potsdam Conference, Stalin agreed to enter the war against Japan. Until this point, the Soviets had not been involved in the war in the Pacific.

On August 6, as President Truman sailed back to the United States from Europe, an American plane dropped an atomic bomb on Hiroshima, Japan. The bomb totally destroyed the city. Three days later, they dropped another bomb, this time on the city of Nagasaki. On August 10, Japan had had enough and asked for peace. It formally surrendered on September 2, 1945.

Postwar Foreign Policies

In April 1945, just a few days after becoming president, Truman had gone to San Francisco, California, to attend the international conference that established the United Nations. The hope that nations would be able to work in harmony after such a horrible world war soon faded; relations between the United States and its wartime ally, the Soviet Union, quickly began to deteriorate.

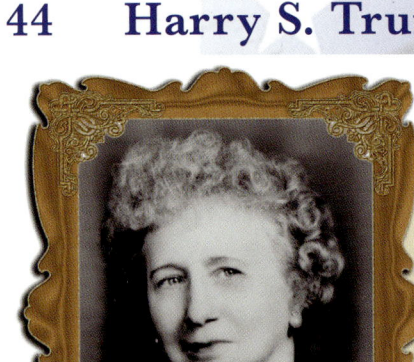

First Lady Elizabeth Truman

Elizabeth "Bess" Virginia Wallace was born in Independence, Missouri, in 1885, the daughter of David and Madge Gates Wallace. Bess was an avid athlete. By the time she was a young woman, she was a skilled tennis player.

Bess Wallace met Harry Truman in Sunday school when he was six and she was five. They attended school together through high school. They were engaged by 1917. Bess's mother, however, felt that Harry was beneath the Wallaces' social class; she was never happy with the match.

Finally, in 1919, Harry and Bess were married. In 1924, their only child, Mary Margaret, was born.

When Harry entered politics in the 1920s, Bess supported him from the sidelines. She was a highly intelligent woman with opinions on issues, but she hated being in the spotlight. Above all, she enjoyed a measure of independence in her life, and she frequently took trips alone back to Missouri during Truman's years in Washington, D.C.

Bess was horrified to find herself the First Lady in April 1945. She was concerned that she would be forced to take an active public role, as had her predecessor, Eleanor Roosevelt. She soon decided, however, that she would just be herself. Unlike Mrs. Roosevelt, Bess gave no press conferences and confined her role to the social responsibilities of First Lady.

Harry Truman was fiercely devoted to Bess. In his memoirs, he wrote that he discussed all major decisions with "the Boss," as he called her. Bess Truman's influence on these decisions is unknown, however, since she never wrote or spoke about their relationship.

After leaving the White House, Bess returned to Independence. She remained active well into her nineties. Bess Truman died in 1982, at the age of 97.

The fear of the spread of Communism around the world created tension. Even before the war had ended in Europe, Stalin had installed Communist governments in many Eastern European countries. This violated the Yalta agreement, which called for free elections in these countries.

When Soviet-backed Communist movements in Greece and Turkey threatened those countries in 1947, President Truman acted. He asked Congress for 400 million dollars in aid to both countries to stop the spread of Communism. The policy of providing aid to challenge the threat of Communism became known as the Truman Doctrine.

Another key postwar aid program was the Marshall Plan, named after Secretary of State George C. Marshall. The Marshall Plan gave more than 13 billion dollars in aid between 1948 and 1952 to the war-ravaged nations of Europe to help them rebuild. Truman offered aid to the nations of Eastern Europe. Stalin, however, refused to allow them to participate.

To defend Western Europe against the threat of Soviet invasion, the Truman administration and the free nations of Europe established the North Atlantic Treaty Organization (NATO) in 1949. NATO was an alliance in which each member agreed to come to the aid of others if they were under attack.

Truman signs the North Atlantic Treaty proclamation.

Postwar Domestic Policies and the Election of 1948

With the end of the war, many American labor unions wanted raises for their members. During the war, wages and prices had been frozen as a part of government price controls. The pressure from labor unions led to numerous strikes, workers' refusal to work, in the first year after the war.

By January 1946, more than 1.5 million workers in the steel, automobile, electrical, and food industries were on strike. In April, the mine workers went on strike. Truman was sympathetic to labor, but he would not allow strikes to disrupt the country.

When railroad workers shut down the nation's railroads in May 1946, Truman ordered the government to seize the rail lines. Truman supported labor throughout his presidency, but he never allowed strikes to hurt the interests of the nation as a whole.

Words to Know

Truman Doctrine (TROO-muhn DOK-trin): A policy of the Truman administration, starting in 1947, that opposed Communist aggression.

Marshall Plan (MAHR-shuhl PLAN): A U.S. sponsored aid program to European nations begun in 1948 to help them recover from World War II.

North Atlantic Treaty Organization (NATO) (NORTH at-LAN-tik TREE-tee or-guh-nuh-ZAY-shuhn): A military alliance between United States and Western European nations for protection against Soviet or other threats. It was established in 1949.

Truman called his domestic program the "Fair Deal." He supported the right of workers to unionize, a fair minimum wage, and civil rights legislation. Acting on his beliefs, Truman, with the stroke of a pen, desegregated the armed forces, which up until the late 1940s had separate African American and white units.

The labor unrest as well as shortages of such key items as housing, clothing, and automobiles contributed to the Republicans winning control of Congress in elections in 1946. To many observers, it seemed as if the 14-year reign of the Democratic Party, which had begun with the election of Franklin Roosevelt in 1932, was about to come to an end.

Unlike Roosevelt, Harry Truman was not a particularly popular president. He often used undiplomatic language and bluntly told people what he thought of them. For example, he once told a journalist whose reporting was critical of him that he would like to punch him in the face. Such statements made Truman seem petty and unpresidential.

Despite the lack of enthusiasm for Truman, the Democrats had no other candidate to offer, and Truman received the nomination for a full term at the 1948 Democratic Convention. To fill the vacant office of vice president, which remained vacant since Roosevelt's death, the convention selected Senator Alben Barkley of Kentucky. At the moment of Truman's nomination, southern delegates walked out of the convention because of a civil rights statement in the Democratic platform.

These southerners then nominated Strom Thurmond, a renegade Democratic governor of South Carolina, to run for president on the States' Rights ("Dixiecrat") ticket. Truman, the Democrats now realized, would lose the once-solid Democratic South. To most observers, his reelection seemed impossible.

President Truman speaks from the rear platform of his train in East St. Louis, Illinois.

The Republicans renominated Governor Thomas E. Dewey, who had run against Roosevelt and lost in 1944. This time, however, all the polls said that Dewey was a sure winner for the presidential slot. Because Dewey seemed so far ahead of Truman, most organizations stopped taking public-opinion surveys after September 1948, saying that it was a waste of money.

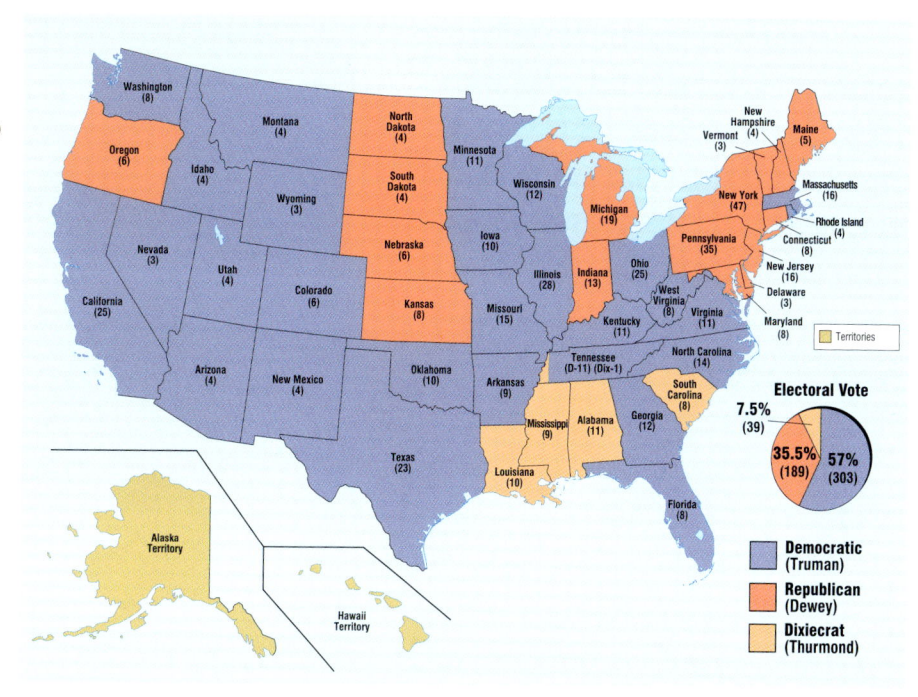

Dewey, convinced that he would win, conducted a low-key campaign that rarely mentioned Truman's name. Newspapers carried articles about what "President Dewey" would do after January 1949.

Most Democrats were convinced that Truman would lose. Truman, however, always believed that he would win, and he embarked on a vigorous campaign by train across the country. Unlike Dewey, Truman blasted his opponents by name, especially the "do-nothing 80th Congress." Speaking from the rear platform of his train, Truman traveled through cities and small towns all across America attacking the Republicans as the party of the rich.

On election night, Truman listened to radio reports insisting that he would lose,

Although predicted to lose the 1948 presidential election, Truman won with 303 electoral votes.

even though he was a million votes ahead of Dewey. The Chicago Tribune even ran its early edition with the headline "Dewey Defeats Truman," but by later that morning, Truman had won.

In one of the greatest upsets in American political history, Truman received 303 electoral votes to Dewey's 189. Truman, the "accidental president" in 1945, was now president in his own right.

The Second Term: Korea and McCarthyism

The promise of Truman's second term was clouded by a war in Asia that embroiled the United States for three years and cost the lives of almost 35,000 American soldiers. In June 1950, the armies of Communist North Korea invaded neighboring South Korea, which was allied with the free world.

Remembering that the failure to respond to Adolf Hitler's aggression in the 1930s had led to world war, Truman urged the United Nations to send a force to Korea to fight the North Korean invasion. The UN peacekeeping force was actually largely an American army. A World War II hero, General Douglas MacArthur, led it.

After a series of early successes by UN forces against the North Koreans, the war was bogged down in a stalemate with no side winning or losing. General MacArthur urged the bombing and invasion of Communist China, which was supplying weapons and soldiers to the North Koreans.

President Truman, however, was afraid of the conflict escalating into a third world war, and he refused to allow any military action against Chinese territory. MacArthur complained in public, and Truman, in one of the most unpopular acts of his presidency, fired the general for insubordination in 1951.

On the domestic front, the war helped increase a fear of Communism. A senator from Wisconsin, Joseph McCarthy, exploited this fear by saying that he had a list of people in government who were Communist spies. McCarthy refused to

Joseph McCarthy

make this list public, but he began holding hearings to expose Communism in all parts of American life. The term McCarthyism has come to mean unfounded and damaging accusations against innocent people.

Many politicians were afraid of Senator McCarthy because of his popularity with the American people. Truman, however, criticized him. In so doing, the president increased his own unpopularity. McCarthy's tactics eventually disgraced him and the U.S. Senate denounced, or criticized him for those tactics.

As the 1952 presidential election approached, Truman, now 68, was eligible to run for a third term. In March 1952, however, he announced that he would retire. A Republican, Dwight D. Eisenhower, and the former commander of American forces in Europe succeeded Truman during World War II. On January 20, 1953, Bess and Harry Truman left the White House and returned to their family home in Independence, Missouri.

Words to Know

McCarthyism (muh-KAHR-thee-iz-uhm): A term referring to unfounded and damaging accusations made against an opponent. The term stems from Joseph McCarthy accusing people of being Communists.

President Truman wishes good luck to General Eisenhower.

After the White House

Harry Truman lived almost another 20 years after leaving the presidency. He enjoyed a quiet life and rarely made public statements. Most of his time was devoted to his presidential library in Independence, where he maintained an office. In 1956, he and Bess toured Europe, where heads of state as well as the European people greeted them enthusiastically.

In retirement, Truman's reputation as a great president grew. By the time of his death at age 88 in 1972; The American people idolized him as a courageous and honest man who had made some of the most difficult decisions ever facing a president.

The Presidency at the Dawn of the Atomic Age

When Herbert Hoover entered the White House in 1929, the United States had a small army and navy but no air force. When Harry Truman left the White House 24 years later, the United States was the greatest power on Earth, with the world's largest military machine and hundreds of nuclear weapons.

And during that time, though the country experienced an economic depression and fought in a world war, democracy survived and prospered and presidential power expanded to new heights.

The Hoover Legacy

Herbert Hoover was a man brimming with ideas about how to make government more efficient. He put many innovative programs in place during his political career.

World War I veterans block the steps of the Capitol during the Bonus March, July 5, 1932.

Military personnel observe a nuclear weapons test at a Nevada test site in 1951.

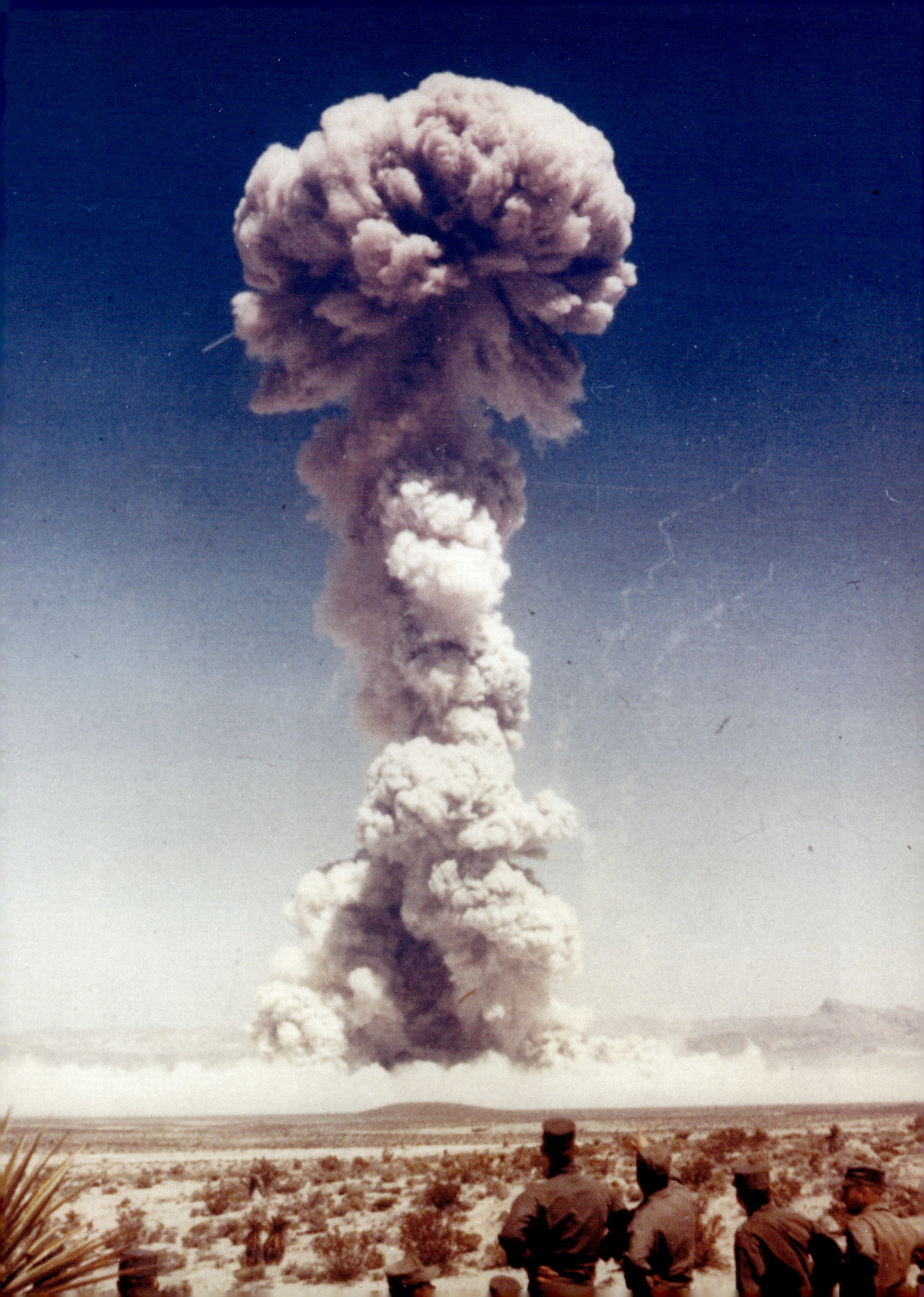

The Presidency at the Dawn of the Atomic Age

President Hoover worked from dawn until dusk. As the Depression worsened, he worked even harder. In the end, though, this well-intended effort meant little. The modern presidency was about leadership, not long hours. Hoover had failed to inspire the American people, who conveyed their need for leadership when they voted Hoover out of office in 1932. In retirement, people came to respect Hoover as a highly intelligent, patriotic American who had done his best to help his country.

The Roosevelt Legacy

Franklin Roosevelt was the most towering president of the twentieth century. He changed the relationship of the government with the American people. Before 1933, Americans had not looked for federal help of any kind. Because of Roosevelt and his New Deal, however, Americans came to see the government as a potential employer and provider.

The New Deal brought jobs and relief to millions of Americans. It did not, however, end the Depression. The Depression ended because of World War II. During the war, the nation's economy was devoted to production of weapons and other materials necessary to win the conflict. Roosevelt presided over an enormous change in America and in the presidency.

The war increased the powers and size of the presidential office enormously. The presidency would never be the same again, nor would the world. Roosevelt gave permission for physicists to develop an atomic bomb. When he died, the bomb was near completion. No one knew whether or not it would work. But, everyone understood that, if it did, it would usher in a new era.

A woman works on an airplane motor on the assembly line at an aviation plant during World War II.

The Presidency at the Dawn of the Atomic Age

Truman reads the announcement of Japanese surrender on August 14, 1945.

The Truman Legacy

Harry Truman was the first atomic-age president. It was he who had to decide whether or not to use the atomic bomb against Japan. And it was he who had to decide whether or not to build an arsenal of nuclear weapons as the basis of America's defenses.

Domestically, Truman continued the social programs of the New Deal and tried to expand civil rights for African Americans. By the end of his presidency, certain New Deal programs were so well established that no one would attempt to eliminate them.

Truman's administration helped create a postwar world political order that lasted for more than 40 years. He decided to stand up to Soviet threats through defense of Greece and Turkey, the Marshall Plan, and NATO. He was also willing to commit American forces to resist Communist military aggression in Korea. The Cold War was defined by his administration.

Cabinet Members

Hoover

VICE PRESIDENT
Charles Curtis

SECRETARY OF STATE
Frank B. Kellogg
Henry L. Stimson

SECRETARY OF THE TREASURY
Andrew W. Mellon
Ogden L. Mills

SECRETARY OF WAR
James W. Good
Patrick J. Hurley

ATTORNEY GENERAL
William D. Mitchell

POSTMASTER GENERAL
Walter F. Brown

SECRETARY OF THE NAVY
Charles F. Adams

SECRETARY OF THE INTERIOR
Ray Lyman Wilbur

SECRETARY OF AGRICULTURE
Arthur M. Hyde

SECRETARY OF COMMERCE
Robert P. Lamont
Roy D. Chapin

SECRETARY OF LABOR
James J. Davis
William N. Doak

Roosevelt

VICE PRESIDENT
John Nance Garner
Henry A. Wallace
Harry S. Truman

SECRETARY OF STATE
Cordell Hull
E. R. Stettinius, Jr.

SECRETARY OF THE TREASURY
William H. Woodin
Henry Morgenthau, Jr.

SECRETARY OF WAR
George H. Dern
Harry H. Woodring
Henry L. Stimson

ATTORNEY GENERAL
Homer S. Cummings
Frank Murphy
Robert H. Jackson
Francis Biddle

POSTMASTER GENERAL
James A. Farley
Frank C. Walker

SECRETARY OF THE NAVY
Claude A. Swanson
Charles Edison
Frank Knox
James Forrestal

SECRETARY OF THE INTERIOR
Harold L. Ickes

SECRETARY OF AGRICULTURE
Henry A. Wallace
Claude R. Wickard

SECRETARY OF COMMERCE
Daniel C. Roper
Harry L. Hopkins
Jesse H. Jones
Henry A. Wallace

SECRETARY OF LABOR
Frances Perkins

Cabinet Members

Truman

VICE PRESIDENT
Alben W. Barkley

SECRETARY OF STATE
E. R. Stettinius, Jr.
James F. Byrnes
George C. Marshall
Dean Acheson

SECRETARY OF THE TREASURY
Henry Morgenthau, Jr.
Frederick M. Vinson
John W. Snyder

SECRETARY OF DEFENSE
James Forrestal
Louis A. Johnson
George C. Marshall
Robert A. Lovett

ATTORNEY GENERAL
Francis Biddle
Tom C. Clark
J. Howard McGrath
James P. McGranery

POSTMASTER GENERAL
Frank C. Walker
Robert E. Hannegan
Jesse M. Donaldson

SECRETARY OF THE INTERIOR
Harold L. Ickes
Julius A. Krug
Oscar L. Chapman

SECRETARY OF AGRICULTURE
Claude R. Wickard
Clinton P. Anderson
Charles F. Brannan

SECRETARY OF COMMERCE
Henry A. Wallace
W. Averell Harriman
Charles Sawyer

SECRETARY OF LABOR
Frances Perkins
Lewis B. Schwellenbach
Maurice J. Tobin

SECRETARY OF WAR
Henry L. Stimson
Robert P. Patterson
Kenneth C. Royall

SECRETARY OF THE NAVY
James Forrestal

Timeline

1770

1774 — First Continental Congress

1775 — American Revolution begins

1776 — America declares independence from Great Britain

1780

1783 — Treaty of Paris formally ends American Revolution

1787 — U.S. Constitution is written

1789 — George Washington becomes president

1790

1791 — Bill of Rights becomes part of Constitution

1793 — Eli Whitney invents cotton gin

1797 — John Adams becomes president

1800

1800 — Washington, D.C., becomes permanent U.S. capital

1801 — Thomas Jefferson becomes president

1803 — Louisiana Purchase almost doubles size of the United States

1808 — Slave trade ends

1809 — James Madison becomes president

1810

1812 — War of 1812 begins

1814 — British burn Washington, D.C. War of 1812 fighting ends

1815 — Treaty of Ghent officially ends War of 1812

1817 — James Monroe becomes president

1820

1820 — Missouri Compromise is passed

1823 — Monroe Doctrine is issued

1825 — John Quincy Adams becomes president

1828 — Popular votes used for first time to help elect a president

1829 — Andrew Jackson becomes president

Timeline

1830

1830 — Congress passes Indian Removal Act

1832 — Samuel Morse has idea for telegraph

1835 — Samuel Colt patents revolver

1837 — Martin Van Buren becomes president

1838 — Native Americans are forced to move to Oklahoma traveling Trail of Tears

1840

1841 — William Henry Harrison becomes president; John Tyler becomes president

1845 — James Polk becomes president

1845 — Texas is annexed to United States

1846 — Mexican War begins; Boundary between Canada and United States is decided

1848 — Gold is discovered in California; First women's rights convention is held

1849 — Zachary Taylor becomes president

1850

1850 — Millard Fillmore becomes president

1850 — Compromise of 1850 is passed

1853 — Franklin Pierce becomes president

1857 — James Buchanan becomes president

1860

1860 — Southern states begin to secede from Union

1861 — Abraham Lincoln becomes president

1863 — Abraham Lincoln gives Gettysburg Address

1865 — Andrew Johnson becomes president

1865 — Civil War ends; Freedman's Bureau is created; 13th Amendment abolishes slavery

1868 — Impeachment charges are brought against President Johnson

1869 — Ulysses S. Grant becomes president

1870

1873 — U.S. economy collapses; depression begins

1876 — Alexander Graham Bell invents telephone

1877 — Rutherford B. Hayes becomes president

1879 — Thomas Edison invents lightbulb

1880

1881 — James Garfield becomes president; Chester Arthur becomes president

1882 — Chinese Exclusion Act restricts number of Chinese immigrants allowed into United States

1885 — Grover Cleveland becomes president

1889 — Benjamin Harrison becomes president

Timeline

1890

- **1890** U.S. troops kill more than 200 Sioux and Cheyenne at Wounded Knee
- **1893** Grover Cleveland becomes president again
- **1893** Charles and J. Frank Duryea construct first car in the United States
- **1897** William McKinley becomes president
- **1898** Spanish-American War occurs

1900

- **1901** Theodore Roosevelt becomes president
- **1903** Orville and Wilbur Wright fly their plane at Kitty Hawk, North Carolina
- **1908** Henry Ford produces Model T
- **1909** William H. Taft becomes president

1910

- **1913** Woodrow Wilson becomes president
- **1914** Panama Canal opens
- **1917** America enters World War I
- **1919** World War I ends

1920

- **1920** 19th Amendment gives women right to vote
- **1921** Warren Harding becomes president
- **1923** Calvin Coolidge becomes president
- **1927** Charles Lindbergh makes first nonstop flight across Atlantic
- **1929** Herbert Hoover becomes president
- **1929** Stock market crashes; America enters economic depression

1930

- **1933** Franklin D. Roosevelt becomes president
- **1939** World War II begins

1940

- **1941** Pearl Harbor is bombed; America enters World War II
- **1945** Harry S. Truman becomes president
- **1945** United States drops atomic bombs on Hiroshima and Nagasaki; World War II ends United Nations is formed

Timeline

1950

- **1950** Korean War begins
- **1953** Dwight Eisenhower becomes president
- **1953** Korean War ends
- **1954** Supreme Court orders desegregation of schools
- **1957** Soviet Union launches *Sputnik I*
- **1958** United States launches *Explorer I*; NASA is created

1960

- **1961** John F. Kennedy becomes president
- **1962** Cuban Missile Crisis
- **1963** Lyndon Johnson becomes president
- **1964** Civil Rights Act of 1964 is passed
- **1965** First U.S. troops sent to Vietnam War
- **1968** Martin Luther King, Jr. is assassinated
- **1969** Richard Nixon becomes president
- **1969** Neil Armstrong is first person to walk on moon

1970

- **1970** First Earth Day is celebrated
- **1973** OPEC places oil embargo resulting in fuel shortages
- **1974** Nixon is first president to resign
- **1974** Gerald Ford becomes president
- **1975** War in Vietnam ends
- **1976** America celebrates its bicentennial
- **1977** Jimmy Carter becomes president
- **1978** Leaders of Israel and Egypt sign the Camp David Accords
- **1979** U.S. embassy in Iran is attacked and hostages are taken

1980

- **1981** Ronald Reagan becomes president
- **1981** American hostages are released; Reagan appoints first woman to Supreme Court, Sandra Day O'Connor
- **1986** U.S. space shuttle *Challenger* explodes after lift-off
- **1989** George H. W. Bush becomes president

1990

- **1991** Persian Gulf War occurs
- **1992** U.S. troops are sent to Somalia to lead multinational relief force; Riots explode in Los Angeles
- **1993** William J. Clinton becomes president
- **1993** World Trade Center is bombed by terrorists
- **1995** Bomb destroys federal building in Oklahoma City
- **1998** U.S. bombs Iraq; Impeachment charges are brought against President Clinton
- **1999** First balanced budget in 30 years is passed; Impeachment trial ends

2000

- **2000** Clinton sets aside land for national parks and monuments; Outcome of the presidential race is clouded due to voting miscounts
- **2001** George W. Bush becomes president
- **2001** Terrorist Attack on the World Trade Center; President Bush announces War on Terrorism
- **2002** No Child Left Behind Act is signed into law
- **2003** U.S. troops are sent to Iraq
- **2009** Barack Obama becomes president

Presidents of the United States

President	Birth	Party	Term	Death
George Washington	February 22, 1732; Westmoreland Cty., VA	None	April 30, 1789 - March 4, 1797	December 14, 1799; Mt. Vernon, VA
John Adams	October 30, 1735; Braintree (Quincy), MA	Federalist	March 4, 1797 - March 4, 1801	July 4, 1826; Quincy, MA
Thomas Jefferson	April 13, 1743; Abermarle Cty., VA	Democratic-Republican	March 4, 1801 - March 4, 1809	July 4, 1826; Charlottesville, VA
James Madison	March 16, 1751; Port Conway, VA	Democratic-Republican	March 4, 1809 - March 4, 1817	June 28, 1836; Orange County, VA
James Monroe	April 28, 1758; Westmoreland Cty., VA	Democratic-Republican	March 4, 1817 - March 4, 1825	July 4, 1831; New York, NY
John Quincy Adams	July 11, 1767; Braintree (Quincy), MA	Democratic-Republican	March 4, 1825 - March 4, 1829	February 23, 1848; Washington, D.C
Andrew Jackson	March 15, 1767; Waxhaw, SC	Democratic	March 4, 1829 - March 4, 1837	June 8, 1845; Nashville, TN
Martin Van Buren	December 5, 1782; Kinderhook, NY	Democratic	March 4, 1837 - March 4, 1841	July 24, 1862; Kinderhook, NY
William Henry Harrison	February 9, 1773; Berkeley, VA	Whig	March 4, 1841 - April 4, 1841	April 4, 1841; Washington, D.C.
John Tyler	March 29, 1790; Charles City Cty., VA	Whig	April 4, 1841 - March 4, 1845	January 18, 1862; Richmond, VA
James Polk	November 2, 1795; Mecklenburg Cty., NC	Democratic	March 4, 1845 - March 4, 1849	June 15, 1849; Nashville, TN
Zachary Taylor	November 24, 1784; Orange Cty., VA	Whig	March 4, 1849 - July 9, 1850	July 9, 1850; Washington, D.C.
Millard Fillmore	January 7, 1800; Locke Township, NY	Whig	July 9, 1850 - March 4, 1853	March 8, 1874; Buffalo, NY
Franklin Pierce	November 23, 1804; Hillsborough, NH	Democratic	March 4, 1853 - March 4, 1857	October 8, 1869; Concord, NH
James Buchanan	April 23, 1791; Cove Gap, PA	Democratic	March 4, 1857 - March 4, 1861	June 1, 1868; Lancaster, PA
Abraham Lincoln	February 12, 1809; Hardin Cty., KY	Republican	March 4, 1861 - April 15, 1865	April 15, 1865; Washington, D.C.
Andrew Johnson	December 29, 1808; Raleigh, NC	Republican	April 15, 1865 - March 4, 1869	July 31, 1875; Carter County, TN
Ulysses S. Grant	April 27, 1822; Point Pleasant, OH	Republican	March 4, 1869 - March 4, 1877	July 23, 1885; Mount McGregor, NY
Rutherford B. Hayes	October 4, 1822; Delaware, OH	Republican	March 4, 1877 - March 4, 1881	January 17, 1893; Fremont, OH
James Garfield	November 18, 1831; Orange, OH	Republican	March 4, 1881 - September 19, 1881	September 19, 1881; Elberon, NJ
Chester Arthur	October 5, 1830; North Fairfield, VT	Republican	September 20, 1881 - March 4, 1885	November 18, 1886; New York, NY
Grover Cleveland	March 18, 1837; Caldwell, NJ	Democratic	March 4, 1885 - March 4, 1889; March 4, 1893 - March 4, 1897	June 24, 1908; Princeton, NJ

Presidents of the United States

President	Birth	Party	Term	Death
Benjamin Harrison	August 20, 1833; North Bend, OH	Republican	March 4, 1889 - March 4, 1893	March 13, 1901; Indianapolis, IN
William McKinley	January 29, 1843; Niles OH	Republican	March 4, 1897 - September 14, 1901	September 14, 1901; Buffalo, NY
Theodore Roosevelt	October 27, 1858; New York, NY	Republican	September 14, 1901 - March 4, 1909	January 6, 1919; Oyster Bay, NY
William H. Taft	September 15, 1857; Cincinnati, OH	Republican	March 4, 1909 - March 4, 1913	March 8, 1930; Washington, D.C.
Woodrow Wilson	December 28, 1856; Staunton, VA	Democratic	March 4, 1913 - March 4, 1921	February 3, 1924; Washington, D.C.
Warren Harding	November 2, 1865; Corsica, OH	Republican	March 4, 1921 - August 2, 1923	August 2, 1923; San Francisco, CA
Calvin Coolidge	July 4, 1872; Plymouth, VT	Republican	August 3, 1923 - March 4, 1929	January 5, 1933; Northampton, MA
Herbert Hoover	August 10, 1874; West Branch, IA	Republican	March 4, 1929 - March 4, 1933	October 20, 1964; New York, NY
Franklin D. Roosevelt	January 30, 1882; Hyde Park, NY	Democratic	March 4, 1933 - April 12, 1945	April 12, 1945; Warm Springs, GA
Harry S. Truman	May 8, 1884; Lamar, MO	Democratic	April 12, 1945 - January 20, 1953	December 26, 1972; Kansas City, MO
Dwight Eisenhower	October 14, 1890; Denison, TX	Republican	January 20, 1953 - January 20, 1961	March 28, 1969; Washington, D.C.
John F. Kennedy	May 29, 1917; Brookline, MA	Democratic	January 20, 1961 - November 22, 1963	November 22, 1963; Dallas, TX
Lyndon Johnson	August 27, 1908; Stonewall, TX	Democratic	November 22, 1963 - January 20, 1969	January 22, 1973; San Antonio, TX
Richard Nixon	January 9, 1913; Yorba Linda, CA	Republican	January 20, 1969 - August 9, 1974	April 22, 1994; New York, NY
Gerald Ford	July 14, 1913; Omaha, NE	Republican	August 9, 1974 - January 20, 1977	December 26, 2006; Rancho Mirage, CA
Jimmy Carter	October 1, 1924; Plains, GA	Democratic	January 20, 1977 - January 20, 1981	
Ronald Reagan	February 6, 1911; Tampico, IL	Republican	January 20, 1981 - January 20, 1989	June 5, 2004; Bel Air, CA
George H. W. Bush	June 12, 1924; Milton, MA	Republican	January 20, 1989 - January 20, 1993	
William J. Clinton	August 19, 1946; Hope, AR	Democratic	January 20, 1993 - January 20, 2001	
George W. Bush	July 6, 1946; New Haven, CT	Republican	January 20, 2001 - January 20, 2009	
Barack Obama	August 4, 1961 Honolulu, Hawaii	Democratic	January 20, 2009 -	

Index

A
Agricultural Adjustment Act, 27, 30
allies, 33, 35
Army, U.S., 17, 37
atomic, 9, 38, 42-43, 50, 52-53, 58

B
banks, 15, 17, 27
Barkley, Alben W., 38, 46, 55
Belgium, 13, 18
Bonus Army, 17
business, 6, 8, 12, 13, 15, 17, 33, 35, 40

C
cabinet, 3, 13, 14, 42, 54-55
China, 12, 16, 30, 48
Churchill, Winston, 35, 43
Civilian Conservation Corps, 27
civil rights, 46, 53, 59
Cold War, 53
Communism, 44, 45, 48
Congress, 27, 30-35, 45-47, 56, 57
Coolidge, Calvin, 4, 9, 14, 58, 61
Cox, James, 23
Curtis, Charles, 10, 14, 18, 54

D
Democratic Party, 14, 29, 33, 41, 46
Dewey, Thomas E., 36, 47
dust storm, 17

E
economy, 4, 6, 15, 17, 52, 56, 57
Eisenhower, Dwight, 48, 49, 59, 61
elections, presidential
   of 1928, 4, 14, 15
   of 1932, 18, 26
   of 1936, 30
   of 1940, 33
   of 1944, 36, 37, 42
   of 1948, 45, 47
   of 1952, 48
electoral, 14, 15, 26, 27, 30, 33, 36, 47
   College, 26, 27
   map, 15, 26, 30, 33, 36, 47
   vote(s), 15, 26, 27, 30, 33, 36, 47
Emergency Relief Act (1932), 17
Europe, 13, 18, 31, 32, 34, 35, 42-45, 48, 49

F
Fair Deal program, 46
farmer(s), 15, 17, 25, 27
federal government, 6, 16, 28
fireside chats, 27
France, 13, 32, 35, 40

G
Garner, John Nance, 20, 26, 33, 54
Germany, 6, 31-35, 37, 38, 42, 43
Great Britain, 43, 56
Great Depression, 4, 6, 7, 9, 17, 20
Greece, 45, 53

H
Harding, Warren, 4, 13, 14, 23, 58, 61
Hitler, Adolf, 31, 32, 48
Hoover, Herbert, 3, 4, 6, 10-19, 25, 26, 50, 52, 54, 58, 61
   born, 10, 12, 61
   died, 10, 19, 61
   First Lady, 10, 16
   term, 10, 61
   vice president, 10, 14, 54
Hoover, Lou Henry, 16
Hoovervilles, 19

I
industries, 6, 35, 45

J
Japan, 6, 9, 31, 32, 34, 35, 37, 38, 42, 43, 53

K
Korea, 47, 48, 53
Korean War, 59

L
labor, 8, 27, 45, 46
Landon, Alfred, 30
League of Nations, 36
Lincoln, Abraham, 37, 57, 60

M
MacArthur, Douglas, 48
Marshall, George C., 45, 53, 55
Marshall Plan, 45, 53
McCarthy, Joseph, 47-48
McCarthyism, 47-48
military, U.S., 8, 35, 40, 45, 48, 50, 53

N
National Recovery Administration, 27, 30
Navy, U.S., 22, 50
New Deal, 27, 28, 30, 31, 33, 41, 52, 53
North Atlantic Treaty Organization, 45
   (NATO), 45
nuclear weapons, 9, 50, 53

O
on margin, 7, 15

Index

P

Pearl Harbor, 34, 58
Poland, 32
polio, 20, 23, 24, 26, 28
Potsdam Conference, 43
prohibition, 14

R

radio, 14, 27, 47
Reconstruction Finance, 17
   Corporation,
Republican Party, 4
Roosevelt, Eleanor, 22, 24, 28,
   37, 44
Roosevelt, Franklin D., 3, 6, 8, 9,
   18, 20-37, 38, 41, 42, 44, 46,
   47, 52, 54, 58, 60
      born, 20, 22, 61
      died, 20, 37, 61
      First Lady, 20, 28
      term, 20, 30, 33, 61
      vice president, 20, 26, 33,
         36, 54
Roosevelt, Theodore, 22, 28,
   58, 61

S

Schechter Poultry Corporation v.,
   the United States, 30
Senate, U.S., 22, 41, 42, 48
Smith, Alfred E., 14, 15, 25
Social Security Act, 28, 29, 30, 31
Soviet Union, 33, 35, 43, 59
Stalin, Joseph, 35, 43, 44, 45
stock market crash, 6, 15, 25, 58
strikes, 45
Supreme Court, 30, 31, 59

T

Tennessee Valley Authority, 28
Thurmond, Strom, 46
Truman, Elizabeth Wallace, 44
Truman, Harry S., 9, 38-49, 50, 53,
   55, 58, 61
      born, 38, 40, 61
      died, 38, 49, 61
      First Lady, 38, 44
      term, 38, 47, 61
      vice president, 38, 55
Truman Doctrine, 45
Turkey, 45, 53

U

United Nations, 29, 36, 43, 48, 58

W

Wallace, Henry A., 33, 36, 38, 41
   54, 55
Warm Springs, Georgia, 24, 37,
   42, 61
Willkie, Wendell L., 33
Wilson, Woodrow, 22, 58, 61
Women, World War II efforts, 8, 35
Works Progress Administration, 27
World War I, 13, 17, 22, 36, 40,
   50, 58
World War II, 6, 8, 18, 20, 32, 35,
   41, 42, 45, 48, 52, 58

Y

Yalta conference, 35, 36, 37, 44

Further Reading

Bausum, Ann. *Our Country's Presidents*. National Geographic Children's Books, 2009.

Collard, Sneed B. *Eleanor Roosevelt: Making the World a Better Place*. Marshall Cavendish Inc., 2008.

Landau, Elaine. *The Great Depression*. Children's Press (CT), 2007.

Maupin, Melissa. *Franklin D. Roosevelt*. The Child's World, Inc., 2008.

Pastan, Amy. *Eyewitness First Ladies*. DK Publishing, 2008.

Rodhe, Paul and Beatrice, Paul. *Kids Meet the Presidents*. Cider Mill Press Book Publishers, LLC, 2009.

Rubel, David. *Encyclopedia of the Presidents and Their Times*. Scholastic, Inc., 2009.

Rumsch, BreAnn. *Herbert Hoover*. ABDO Publishing, 2009.

Venezia, Mike. *Harry S. Truman: Thirty-Third President 1945-1953*. Children's Press (CT), 2007.

Websites to Visit

www.enchantedlearning.com/history/us/pres/list.shtml

www.whitehouse.gov/kids

http://pbskids.org/wayback

www.kidinfo.com/American_History/Presidents.html